Also by Patrick McKeown

The Oxygen Advantage: The Simple, Scientifically Proven Breathing Technique for a Healthier, Slimmer, Faster, and Fitter You

Buteyko Mindfulness Method Online Course; Calm your mind, improve concentration, live in the moment, and enjoy freedom from ADD, stress, panic attacks and depression

Buteyko Clinic Method 2hr DVD, CD, Manual; the Complete Instruction to Reverse Asthma, Rhinitis and Snoring Permanently

Buteyko Kids Meet Dr Mew [DVD set]: The Complete Buteyko Breathing Method for Children

Asthma Free Naturally

Sleep with Buteyko: Stop Snoring, Sleep Apnoea and Insomnia

Buteyko Meets Dr Mew [Book]: The Complete Buteyko Breathing Method for Children and Teenagers

ANXIETY FREE:
STOP WORRYING AND QUIETEN YOUR MIND

Improve oxygen delivery to your brain and stop excessive and useless thoughts featuring the Buteyko Breathing Method and mindfulness

PATRICK G MCKEOWN

ButeykoClinic.com

Anxiety free: stop worrying and quieten your mind

Published by: PatrickMcKeown.net
Loughwell, Moycullen, Co Galway
W: www.PatrickMcKeown.net
E: info@PatrickMcKeown.net

© Patrick McKeown 2015

Cover design by Aurora Pérez Machío

Illustrations by Rebecca Burgess

ISBN-10: 0-9545996-4-0

ISBN-13: 978-0-9545996-4-5

Contents

Chapter 4 – Physical exercise to still the mind   **71**

Chapter 5 – Further stilling the mind   **83**

This book is for any person who wishes to have clearer functioning of his or her mind and not to be bogged down with useless thinking. Within three weeks the result will be more control over thoughts, better concentration, more energy, more joy, happiness and appreciation for life. This is a simple and straightforward self-help book approached from two different and yet related perspectives.

The first is about correcting breathing volume using a physician-developed program known as the Buteyko Breathing Method. Chronic overbreathing is a habit present with any person who experiences stress, anxiety, panic attacks and depression. It causes both a constriction of blood vessels and reduced delivery of oxygen to tissues and organs, most notably the brain. The Buteyko Method is a simple approach that significantly improves oxygenation of the brain, resulting in far less brain cell excitability.

The second aspect deals with recognising the activity of the mind, the nature of thought and how to step out of thought. This too is essential to understanding your mind and taking control.

The mind is regarded as the most important capability of the human species, yet most people have little control over it as it races from thought to thought. Mind activity, stress, depression and anxiety are nothing more than the absence of control. How much control do you have over your mind? For how long can you choose to stop thinking?

A quiet mind is one that you have control over. Quite simply, you can choose to think or not to think. You don't get lost in trains of useless thinking. Most of the time, you know what thoughts are taking place in your mind. Without control over our minds, we have nothing. It is the one part of us that determines our quality of life on earth, yet it receives little attention from our educational, religious and medical institutions. How insane is that?

If only you had a chance to look inside people's minds, you would see the same turmoil that goes on inside your own head. Hidden behind the nice white smile is fear of the future and regrets from the past. A racing and repetitive mind is just below the surface. It might not have reached the depths that someone in depression has reached, but at the same time, you will see common traits. In fact, all of us are just a few stressful events away from mental problems. Cumulative stressful events take their toll on everybody unless, of course, we have some understanding of thought processes and can better oxygenate our brain.

In our sophisticated Western world with its emphasis on intelligence and the stigma on mental problems, normal healthy people who go through periods of being down or depressed have few outlets through which to seek help. Addressing this deficit early on is the key to reversing it.

My interest in this area stems from having both asthma and a racing mind for many years. I used the Buteyko Method to reverse my asthma and by improving my awareness, I also addressed my racing mind. Thousands have attended my courses in Ireland and abroad for asthma and other conditions. Those who have attended for panic attacks, depression, stress and anxiety have reported very good results; hence, this book.

This book can be read by someone with poor concentration, or a clouded and depressed mind. It contains nothing complicated and through constant repetition, the reader can apply the guidance provided.

CHAPTER 1
What determines your happiness?

"Thinking is the most unhealthy thing in the world, and people die of it just as they die of any other disease"

— OSCAR WILDE

Psychologists estimate that we have sixty thousand thoughts each day. Moreover, 95% of these thoughts are repetitive and useless. Not knowing the content of our own mind, we are literally at its mercy and unconsciously follow its instruction to the letter.

The habit of excessive thought and more importantly, lack of awareness of what takes place in the mind, are the results of the inherited human mind. Its individual content is created by our past experiences, from societal, educational and social influences and is kept alive through repetition.

In the Western world, thinking is viewed as good and not thinking is viewed as a reflection of laziness or dullness. We often hear about the "brilliant thinkers" who make profound discoveries or realisations. Truth be told, eureka moments are made not during thought but during a cessation of thought.

Our educational system teaches us how to think. Through school and university, the mind is developed and moulded into a superb analytical tool. Thinking is seen as the solution to any of life's situations. If we have a problem, we believe that the more we think about it the greater the chances of it being solved. As children, we did not think. Thinking is a learned habit developed over time.

If you feel that it is good to think a lot, take a look at the stress of people in the constant grip and torture of their minds. Often, I pass by a man on Shop street in Galway. He is so tormented that he openly voices the contents of his mind in the street. His mind has completely taken him over. He is pressed down with thought. He is depressed.

Many of us are similar to the man on the street, except that we don't talk out loud. Instead, we have internal mental chatter. We think about the same thing day in and day out, with little resolve or reduction in thinking. Watch your thoughts and you will have no doubt that the Western human mind is truly mad.

Thinking for practical purposes is fine, as it serves a function. However, most of our thinking is not for practical purposes. Most thinking is spent on insane repetitive worry and anxiety.

If you could eliminate your repetitive thought activity by 50%, you would be very happy indeed. If you could eliminate all repetitive and useless thinking, you would live a life of bliss.

Thinking makes you unhappy. Less thought activity makes you happy. Thinking is a disease.

Control your mind or allow
your mind to control you

Human thinking began tens of thousands of years ago. It is the single most important function that differentiates our ability from animals.

Thinking is very useful for practical situations. We need to remember how to drive a car, decide what choice to take, determine a strategy, plan an event, deal with a specific situation. You might want to go to the shop- you think about what foods are not in the cupboard. You organise flights- you think about best dates, price and destination. You write a letter- you think about what you need to say. You go to the petrol pumps to fill your car- you decide on what pump and how much money to spend. You contact a supplier- you think about what you need, what quantities, what price and when it will be delivered. Somebody might have overcharged you- you decide on what you are going to say and you say it to them. Thinking when used in this instance for practical purposes is fine. It is necessary and is productive.

However, 95% of our thinking is not used to deal with a practical situation. Most thinking is unnecessary and repetitive. You will realise this as you observe the activity of your mind.

You are walking in a beautiful quiet park and instead of experiencing the sun at the back of your head, the beautiful sight of flowers around you and the wonderful sounds of children at play, your attention is wrapped up giving out about your neighbour who gave you a lecture yesterday, or your boss who was unhappy with your work, or the other driver who blew the horn at you, or that you need to pay your mortgage at the end of the month. This kind of thinking is torture. It does nothing to help your situation. It does nothing to help you. Continuously thinking like this will drive you into depression.

You are not only driving yourself insane, you are missing out on the wonders that life has to offer you.

Quietening the mind

Regardless of the extent to which thoughts have taken over, everyone has the capacity to take back control of his or her mind. A still mind is just covered up with mental noise; therefore, anything that helps to de-clutter your mind will allow stillness to resurface.

Your choice is to keep running the thoughts through your head and experience the consequences, or become a good gardener of your mind, root out the weeds and allow only the flowers to grow. A sleeping gardener is not attentive and will soon have a jungle of weeds. A good gardener is awake. He knows exactly what is happening and will guard his territory with a keen eye, removing the weeds as soon as the first shoots appear.

Be a good gardener of your mind. A mind that is being observed is an unsuitable environment for anxiety and depression to take root. Both require a lack of awareness as a suitable breeding ground.

A still mind enables us to relate far better to life and to live life instead of paying attention to useless thinking. No longer is so much of our energy wasted on harmful escapades and we can instead focus with better concentration on what we truly choose. Although learning how to take back control of our mind is very simple, just like the good gardener, attention is required.

Do you want to live a life free from worry and unhappiness?

The next section lists simple self-help breathing and awareness practices that deal with the physiological and psychological aspects of depression, anxiety and stress.

Thinking for practical situations is useful. Thinking that is repetitive and unnecessary is a hindrance.

NOTES:

CHAPTER 2
Introducing the
Buteyko Method -
Overbreathing
and its effects

The Buteyko Method was developed in the 1950's by Russian doctor Konstantin Buteyko. His method has been practiced by hundreds of thousands of people for a variety of conditions including asthma, snoring, sleep apnoea, insomnia, high blood pressure, anxiety, stress, panic attacks and depression.

As a young doctor, Buteyko spent many months sitting at sick patients' bedsides observing their states of health. He noticed that each person's breathing got heavier as his or her health deteriorated. As their illnesses advanced, he saw that his patients' breathing movements from their chests and tummies increased, that their breathing became more audible, that their breaths became faster and that they sighed more and breathed through their mouths. In time, he was able to predict the onset of death just by observing their breathing.

This raised a fundamental question for Buteyko: was it his patients' sickness that contributed to their heavy breathing or was it their heavy breathing that contributed to their sickness?

At the time, Buteyko suffered from very high blood pressure that was going from bad to worse. He began experimenting by breathing less and quietening his breathing. Within a short while, the pains that he had experienced for months went away.

Over the following decades, Buteyko extensively researched this subject and had a dedicated laboratory to further his findings. His method was brought to the West in 1990 and is now taught in many countries.

Breathing, such a vital factor for life, must meet certain conditions. Severe overbreathing can be fatal if sustained over a short period. Therefore, it is plausible to accept that negative health effects will result from less severe but still excessive breathing over a long period.

Normal breathing volume

The number of breaths per minute during normal breathing is about 10 to 12. Each breath is approximately 500 ml. This provides a healthy volume, as described in any university medical textbook, of five to six litres of air per minute. Normal breathing is quiet, still, calm, relaxed and regular.

Persons suffering from anxiety and depression breathe a volume greater than normally accepted amounts. For example, an average sized person with anxiety might breathe 15 to 20 breaths per minute, with each breath larger than the normal 500 ml. Interspersed with this is a number of sighs. Assuming that each breath is 700 ml, the average breathing volume for this person is 10 to 15 litres of air per minute. In food terms, this is akin to eating six to nine meals each day!

Chronic overbreathing

Chronic overbreathing basically means that we habitually breathe more air than what our bodies require. In many ways, this is similar to a person developing the habit of overeating.

Breathing is similar. If we breathe more than what our bodies require over a 24-hour period, the habit takes hold. Dr Stephen Demeter confirms this when he states, "Prolonged hyperventilation (for more than 24 hours) seems to sensitize the brain, leading to a more prolonged hyperventilation." [1]

What increases breathing volume?

Breathing increases as a result of modern living. Factors such as strong emotions, time urgency, tension, anger, stress, anxiety, overeating, processed foods, a belief that taking big breaths is good, lack of exercise, excessive talking and high temperatures within the home all contribute to overbreathing.

How to recognise habitual overbreathing

At this point, you might think that you don't overbreathe. For most people, overbreathing is subtle. It is hidden, which is why it often goes undetected. The typical characteristics of people attending my clinics include:

- » Breathing through the mouth;
- » Audible breathing during rest;
- » Regular sighs;
- » Regular sniffing;
- » Irregular breathing;
- » Holding of the breath (apnoea);
- » Taking large breaths prior to talking;
- » Yawning with big breaths;
- » Upper chest movement;
- » Movement of shoulders while breathing;
- » Lots of visible movement;
- » Effortful breathing;
- » Heavy breathing at night.

How many apply to you? Do you sigh? Do you breathe through your mouth? Do you wake up with a dry mouth in the morning? Does your breathing get faster or chaotic when you are stressed?

Later on, you will be able to measure how well you breathe by using a simple breath hold test developed by Dr Buteyko called the Control Pause. The importance of efficient breathing becomes clear when you understand that breathing too much air into the lungs reduces the amount of oxygen delivered to tissues and organs, including the heart and brain. Over-breathing has a detrimental effect on two gases essential for body oxygenation: nitric oxide and carbon dioxide. In 1991, nitric oxide (NO) was discovered within exhaled air and extensive research revealed that production of the gas takes place both inside the blood vessels and the sinuses surrounding the nasal cavity. When we breathe in through the nose, large amounts of NO are released within the nasal airways. Nitric oxide then follows airflow to the lungs where it helps to dilate the blood vessels and increases oxygen uptake in the blood. Breathing slowly and gently through the nose allows the body to harness the benefits of nasal nitric oxide, while mouth-breathing bypasses this extraordinary gas.

Carbon dioxide (CO_2) is another vital element in correct breathing volume and body oxygenation. CO_2 is a product of metabolism; during the conversion of food and oxygen into energy, carbon dioxide is generated and carried to the lungs where the excess is exhaled. It is crucial, however, that the body retains a quotient of carbon dioxide. Breathing too much removes too much carbon dioxide and causes an imbalance to blood gases. Carbon dioxide is not just a waste gas – it is essential to maintaining correct oxygenation of the body.

Carbon dioxide

Carbon dioxide or CO_2 is a gas created from our metabolic process as an end product. The human lungs require 5% CO_2 or partial pressure of 40 mmHg. If we breathe more than required, too much CO_2 is exhaled or washed from our lungs. An excessive loss of CO_2 from the lungs results in a lowering of CO_2 in the blood, tissues and cells.

The release of oxygen from red blood cells depends on the partial pressure or quantity of carbon dioxide in your lungs/arterial blood. When one is overbreathing, too much carbon dioxide is removed from the body, causing the oxygen to **"stick"** to haemoglobin within the red blood cells. This prevents its release into tissues and organs. This bond, discovered in 1904, is known as the Bohr Effect.

The secret to delivering more oxygen throughout the body is to breathe lightly, or even under-breathe for short periods of time. Breathing a little less than normal allows incoming air to gather a higher concentration of nasal nitric oxide and allows carbon dioxide to accumulate in the blood, opening the airways and blood vessels to increase oxygenation.

While reading this book, some readers may be dismayed to discover that the source of their stress, anxiety, panic attacks and depression is likely to be habitual over-breathing. After all, we are so often told to take deep breaths by well-meaning yoga teachers, Pilates instructors, doctors and stress councillors – but should we be doing the complete opposite? Contrary to popular belief, there is nothing positive to be gained by 'big breaths', since they essentially result in over-breathing, reducing levels of nitric oxide and carbon dioxide. Taking a large breath of fresh air into the lungs might feel good, but this is mostly due to the stretch and subsequent relaxation of your breathing muscles; the action itself doesn't increase the oxygen in your blood. This is because the blood is already almost fully saturated with oxygen during normal breathing; blood oxygen saturation is generally around 97–98% if breathing is light and unnoticeable during rest. And just in case you think there is room for a little more, bear in mind that oxygen is constantly diffusing from the blood to the cells, so having 100% saturation is simply not necessary. In fact, during normal conditions, with a healthy breathing volume of 4-6 litres per minute, 75% of your intake of oxygen is exhaled. Even during intense exercise it is estimated that we exhale 25% of our oxygen intake – a sure sign that we have more than enough oxygen to meet body requirements.

The Bohr Effect
simply explained

Healthy people have quiet and unnoticeable breathing. While they are resting, you cannot see or hear their breathing.

Quiet breathing ensures optimum partial pressure of carbon dioxide within your lungs, blood, tissues and cells. The release of oxygen from your blood depends on the presence of carbon dioxide.

Overbreathing causes too much carbon dioxide to be removed from your lungs, blood, tissues and cells.

This results in less oxygen being released from your blood into your tissues and organs. The more you breathe, the more your body is being starved of oxygen.

Breathing through your mouth, regular sighing and sniffing, noticeable breathing, hearing your breathing during rest or having a low Control Pause (explained later) indicates that you are starving your body of oxygen. Your brain is being starved of oxygen, and this contributes to anxiety, depression and stress.

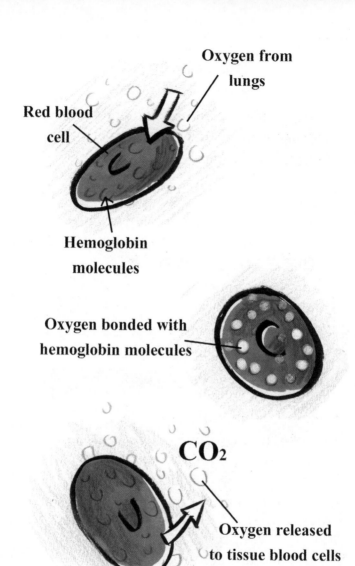

Oxygen from lungs

Red blood cell

Hemoglobin molecules

Oxygen bonded with hemoglobin molecules

CO_2

Oxygen released to tissue blood cells

Normal Blood Flow

Restricted Blood Flow

THE CALMER AND QUIETER YOU BREATHE, THE MORE YOUR BLOOD VESSELS OPEN, ENABLING BETTER CIRCULATION AND DISTRIBUTION OF OXYGEN THROUGHOUT THE BODY, INCLUDING THE BRAIN.

TO IMPROVE OXYGEN DELIVERY TO YOUR BRAIN— BREATHE LESS.

Dilation of blood vessels and airways

Carbon dioxide relaxes the smooth muscles that surround the airways, arteries and capillaries.

With a normal breathing volume of 5 litres of air per minute, the partial pressure of carbon dioxide amounts to 40mmHg. Each 1 mmHg drop of arterial CO_2 reduces blood flow to the brain by 2%.[2] In other words, oxygenation of your brain significantly decreases when you breathe heavily.

The heavier you breathe, the more you feed your hyperventilation or overbreathing related problems. Have you ever noticed that you get light-headed after taking a number of big breaths? Have you ever noticed being very tired in the morning after a night's breathing through the mouth? How tired are you after a day's talking? Do you notice that, as you get stressed, your breathing gets faster, resulting in a mental block and difficulty in making worthwhile decisions? Heavy breathing feeds anxiety and stress.

Overbreathing causes depression, stress and anxiety

Lower carbon dioxide within the blood causes a constriction of the carotid arteries, the main blood vessels going to the brain.

The extent of constriction depends on genetic predisposition but has been estimated by Gibbs (1992) to be as much as 50% for those with anxiety and panic attacks.[3] This finding is also supported by Ball & Shekhar (1997).[4]

Other researchers, including Balestrino and Somjen (1988) [5] and Huttunen et al. (1999),[6] have demonstrated that CO_2 reduces cortical excitability. Cited in Normal Breathing: the key to vital health, "breathing too much makes the human brain abnormally excited due to reduced CO_2 concentrations. As a result, the brain gets literally out of control due to appearance of spontaneous and asynchronous ('self-generated') thoughts." Balestrino and Somjen (1988) in their summary directly claimed that, "The brain, by regulating breathing, controls its own excitability."[7]

Dr Robert Fried, professor of psychology, states that "the first stage of chronic graded hypoxia (insufficient oxygen), which has repeatedly been shown in the case of chronic hyperventilation, is depression of mood and activity."[8]

The late Dr Claude Lum commented that "hyperventilation presents a collection of bizarre and often apparently unrelated symptoms, which may affect any part of the body, and any organ or any system."[9] He further labelled chronic hyperventilation as the fat file syndrome, noting that patients go from doctor to doctor in an attempt to get help for their symptoms. However, because chronic hyperventilation is overlooked in most instances, the patient might be told after a series of tests that there is nothing wrong with him or her, thus increasing the size of the patients' file and further adding to his or her anxiety.

In the late Professor Buteyko's words, "Exhaling Carbon Dioxide from the organism brings about spasms in bronchi, vessels and intestines, etc. This reduces oxygen supply, leading to oxygen deficiency, making one's breath heavier, thus completing the vicious circle."

What is the fat file syndrome?

Louise's personal account:

"For example, because I am prone to worry and overthink things, I get myself worked up into a right state about my symptoms. At different times, I was convinced that I had a brain tumour, MS, a heart problem, bowel cancer, etc. I had blood test after blood test, an ECG test, a scan, and nothing was found to be wrong. My whole family and my doctor, and probably most of my friends, think I'm a hypochondriac... but I knew that something was not right. I just didn't make the connection to my breathing, so my symptoms went on and on and I felt like I was going mad. For lots of people, reading this book will be a real epiphany... and they might need some reassurance early on that they're not alone and not mad after all, and that a lot of their symptoms will go away. Not worrying about the symptoms immediately reduces stress levels and hence breathing."

Stress, anxiety and anger cause overbreathing

According to the famous physiologist Walter Cannon, stress activates the fight or flight response. Meeting deadlines, financial pressures, time urgency, marital issues, the pressure of rearing children and wanting to do well in our work, as well as many other factors, add to stress levels.

Stress ensures survival of the species

Stress is a natural reaction that we have developed throughout our evolution to ensure the survival of our species. Invariably, stress is our body undergoing chemical change in response to environmental conditions. Thousands of years ago, our main threat was from wild animals.

When confronted, we had two options to deal with it. The first was that we fought the animal. The second was that we ran away from it as fast as we could. As our bodies were required to perform intense physical activity, our physiology changed in the following ways:

- » Our breathing volume increases;
- » Our heart rate increases;
- » Adrenaline is pumped into our system;
- » Our pupils dilate;
- » Blood is diverted from our internal organs to our arms and legs;
- » Diarrhoea may occur (lightens our weight before flight);
- » Our blood coagulates in case of injury.

However, today our society and environment have changed at a far greater pace than what our bodies can adjust to. We respond to the stresses of today with the same reaction as we had thousands of years ago. We are in a traffic jam rushing to get to a meeting. The fight or flight response is activated but there is no need for it. Our heart rate increases, blood is diverted to our skeletal muscles, our breathing increases— we are primed for physical activity yet we are sitting still. The result is that we are running on the inside and sitting on the outside.

The heavy breathing arising from the fight or flight response results in a washing out of carbon dioxide from the lungs. This causes a narrowing of blood vessels, thus reducing blood flow to the brain. In addition, the release of oxygen from blood cells is less; the result of the Bohr Effect. This in turn increases self-generated and more random thoughts. With uncontrolled thought activity, we feel unable to cope with our everyday activities, further increasing our stress. A vicious circle has commenced, with stress increasing our breathing and this in turn increasing our stress.

How to correct it

Only by bringing your breathing volume to normal levels can you deal with the physiological aspects of stress and anxiety. Stress causes us to breathe more, so taking a deep breath to calm yourself down just doesn't make any sense, and only serves to keep you in a continued state of stress. Instead, the opposite is needed – slow, quiet, calm breathing that allows blood gases and operating systems to restore to normal. The following responses will give you an idea of the correct way to deal with symptoms of stress:

Stress Activation	Relaxation Activation
Breathing becomes faster	Slow down breathing
More frequent sighing	Suppress sighs if possible
Breathing from the upper chest	Breathe from the tummy
Breathing through the mouth	Breathe through the nose
Breathing becomes more noticeable	Quieten and silence breathing
Breathing becomes erratic	Take slow, gentle, calm, quiet breaths

Long-term stress is exhausting and often the root cause of many illnesses and conditions. I have met many people who led very healthy lives until they experienced significant long term stress. Within six months to a year of increased stress, they were diagnosed with high blood pressure, chronic fatigue and even cancer. When you consider the effect of stress on breathing, this connection makes sense. Stress causes our breathing to become faster and more intense, which reduces the availability of the gases carbon dioxide and nasal nitric oxide, resulting in reduced blood circulation and oxygen delivery. When the body is poorly oxygenated, numerous common conditions and health concerns begin to manifest.

Remember: The more you breathe in, the more you breathe out.

The more you breathe out, the more CO_2 is washed from the lungs.

As CO_2 is washed from the lungs, the partial pressure of CO_2 is reduced in the blood, tissues and cells.

Stress over a period of weeks or months causes prolonged overbreathing, and this resets the respiratory centre in the brain to tolerate a lower partial pressure of CO_2.

Therefore, even when the initial stress is removed, the heavy breathing habit is maintained as a result of chemoreceptors in the brain being reset.

An anxious person may attend many psychotherapists, counsellors, psychologists and psychiatrists in an effort to get to the root of his or her condition. However, unless chronic overbreathing is addressed, he or she will be at a significant disadvantage in making progress.

Breathing a little less than usual for brief periods of time throughout the day helps to harness nasal nitric oxide and normalises the partial pressure of carbon dioxide within the body. Reduced breathing helps to improve oxygen delivery to the brain, resulting in improved sleep, better energy levels and a far calmer disposition.

How many of the following symptoms of hyperventilation do you have?

» Neurological: light-headed feeling, poor concentration, memory lapses, faintness, headache, anxiety, tension, racing mind, numbness and tingling, tremor, depression, apprehension, irritability, brain fog, panic attacks, disrupted sleep, detachment from reality and stress.

» Heart: palpitations, a racing heartbeat, pain in the chest region and a skipping or irregular heartbeat.

» Respiratory system: wheezing, breathlessness, coughing, chest tightness, frequent yawning, snoring and sleep apnoea.

» Gastrointestinal: Esophagal reflux, heartburn, aerophagia.

Other general symptoms include mouth dryness, fatigue, bad dreams, sleep disturbance, nightmarés, dry itchy skin, sweating, cramping, spasm, increased urination such as bed wetting or regular visits to the bathroom during the night, diarrhoea, constipation, general weakness and chronic exhaustion.

CHAPTER 3
Applying Buteyko Breathing

How to interpret breathing exercises

All breathing exercises are accompanied by a line diagram. To interpret each diagram, understanding the following symbols is essential:

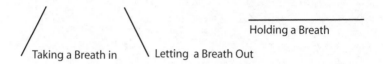

Taking a Breath in   Letting a Breath Out   Holding a Breath

How to interpret breathing instructions

Important: All breathing exercises and the Control Pause, which involves holding the breath, are performed after an exhalation.

Measure breathing volume – your Control Pause

(A free video of this exercise is available from www.ButeykoClinic.com.)

To measure the extent of your relative breathing volume, a very simple breath hold test called the Control Pause (CP) is used. The Control Pause provides feedback on your symptoms and, more importantly, your progress. Your CP measures the length of time that you can comfortably hold your breath.

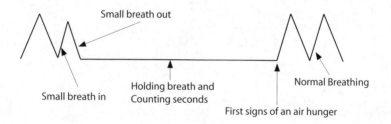

Small breath out

Small breath in   Holding breath and Counting seconds   Normal Breathing

First signs of an air hunger

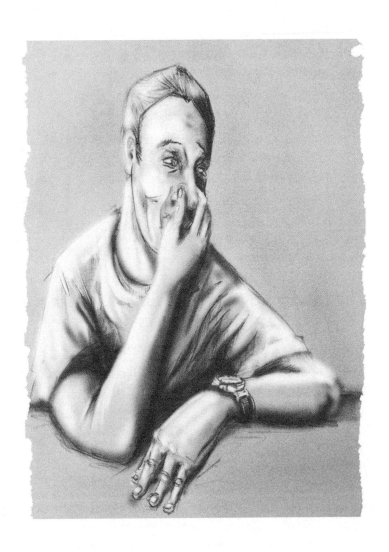

For this you will need a watch or clock with a second hand.

1. Take a small, silent breath in and a small, silent breath out.

2. Hold your nose with your fingers to prevent air from entering your lungs.

3. Count how many seconds until you feel the first signs of air hunger.

4. Your inhalation at the end of the breath hold should be no greater than your breathing prior to taking the measurement.

Release your nose and breathe in through it.

If your breath in is disrupted, then you have held it for too long and have an inaccurate CP.

The following are important points to be aware of before we start:

1. The breath is taken after gently exhaling.

2. The breath is held only until the first urges. It is not a measure of the maximum length of time that you can hold your breath.

3. Your CP only measures your breath hold time. It is not an exercise to correct your breathing.

Remember that taking your CP entails holding your breath only until the first urges. If you had to take a big breath at the end of the breath hold, then you held your breath for too long. The most accurate CP is taken first thing in the morning after waking up.

What does the CP (comfortable breath hold time) mean?

The lower your breath hold time, the greater your breathing volume and symptoms of anxiety. Depending on genetic predisposition, persons who breathe too much are generally more stressed than persons displaying healthy breathing patterns. A person with a high CP is a lot more relaxed and calm than a person with a lower CP. People who experience panic or hyperventilation attacks are invariably big breathers. The objective is to reach a CP of 40 seconds.

The following are essential rules to making progress:

» You will feel better each time your CP increases by five seconds.

» If your CP does not change, you will not feel better.

» From week to week there should be a noticeable improvement of 3-4 seconds in your Control Pause. After that, progress will continue at a slightly slower pace.

» The most accurate CP is taken first thing after waking. This CP is most accurate since you cannot influence your breathing during sleep, and it is based on your breathing volume as set by your respiratory centre.

» Taking your CP throughout the day will give you feedback on your symptoms at those particular times.

» Your goal is to have a morning CP of 40 seconds for six months.

Three steps to increasing your CP

STEP 1. Observe your breathing throughout the day. To stop your big breathing:

    a. Close your mouth and breathe through your nose.

    b. Stop sighing;

    c. Never hear your breathing while resting.

STEP 2. Apply gentle reduced breathing, relaxation and still your mind.

STEP 3. Take physical exercise with correct breathing. (Physical exercise is necessary to increase your CP from 20 to 40 seconds. More details on this are further on.)

STEP 1 is the foundation. Make the change to nasal breathing on a permanent basis, suppress your sighs, be aware of your breathing and ensure that it is quiet throughout the day. A regular sigh is enough to maintain chronic hyperventilation; therefore, it is very important to stop sighing by swallowing or holding your breath. Unless your foundation is strong, your progress will be inadequate. If you sigh and have taken a large breath, then hold your breath for ten seconds to counteract this. You will make progress by keeping your mouth closed but this will not be enough by itself. It is also necessary to reverse the overbreathing habit that you have developed over the years.

Compare our lifestyles

Fifty years ago:	Today:
Greater physical activity	Little physical activity
More natural foods	More processed foods
Less overeating	Habitual overeating
Cooler temperatures within the home	Higher temperatures in homes and warmer clothing
Less public talking	Talking forms a large part of our working life
Less stress, less competitive pressures, a more green environment and nature	More stress, artificial and noisy concrete environment, information overload
Result: Correct volume breathing, higher CP, anxiety and depression uncommon	Result: Big volume breathing, lower CP, anxiety and depression very common

As your CP increases, your breathing volume reduces to more normal levels.

As your breathing volume reduces to more normal levels, your CP increases.

The following is an example of the relationship between your breathing volume and CP.

CP of 10 seconds: breathing is noisy, loud, irregular, large, heavy, erratic and effortful.

Low CP - 10 seconds

CP of 20 seconds: breathing is heavy but calmer and a natural pause occurs between each breath.

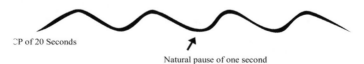

CP of 20 Seconds

Natural pause of one second

CP of 30 seconds: breathing is calm and quiet and the natural pause gets longer.

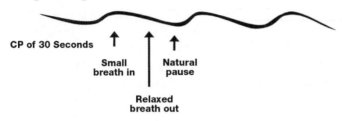

CP of 40 seconds: breathing is very quiet, regular, calm and unnoticeable.

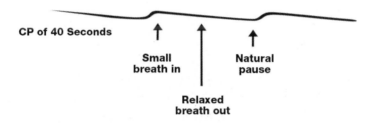

How to know if you are practising breathing exercises correctly

Ultimately, all exercises are designed to correct your breathing and reverse chronic hyperventilation. The goal is for your breathing to become quiet, gentle, calm and regular, as characterized by a high CP.

All exercises involve one thing and that is to breathe less for periods of time throughout the day to reverse the bad habit of overbreathing.

When you practice a breathing exercise, it is necessary that you feel a tolerable and nonstressful hunger for air. This is good feedback and essential to correcting the habit of overbreathing. Feeling a need for air is the result of an increase in CO_2 in your blood. Your respiratory centre is reacting to this increased CO_2 by stimulating your breathing to keep it at a lower level. After nine to twelve minutes of air hunger, the increased CO_2 penetrates the blood–brain barrier and resets the respiratory centre a little. This is indicated by a higher CP taken a few minutes after completing 15–20 minutes of breathing exercises.

Feeling the need for air is not a result of your body being deprived of oxygen. It arises because you are breathing less than you normally do.

> There is just one simple rule and without it, you will make little progress: the only way that you know that you are reducing your breathing is when you feel a need for air.

A need for air is the same as a want for air. The experience of breathlessness is similar to partaking in physical activity.

To experience and understand the need for air, perform the following (the degree of air shortage will depend on the exercises you are undertaking):

» Take a small breath in;

» Gently breathe out;

» Hold your nose and wait until you feel a distinct but non- stressful need to breathe in.

Panicking while reducing your breathing

It can be quite common for people who are prone to anxiety and panic attacks to feel uncomfortable when they first practice reduced breathing exercises.

Depending on your individual health, you might have experienced periods of anxiety and hyperventilation attacks in the past. During these past attacks, as your breathing got faster and more chaotic, you probably experienced a feeling of suffocation or hunger for air.

The following exercises, through creating a need for air, may make you feel uncomfortable. However, know that there is a significant difference between the hunger for air from your attacks in the past and the hunger for air that is created through reduced breathing exercises. This time, you have complete control over your air hunger and can alter it at will.

Gently subjecting the body to the feeling of air hunger for short periods of time will also reduce the body's fear response, reducing the risk of panic and hyperventilation. After all, the sensation of air hunger is a natural occurrence that we experience several times a day, especially during physical exercise, and there is no need for the body to respond to the feeling with panic.

To help with this, practice the exercises gently and feel a need for air no greater than what you would experience during a mild walk. Start off by gently reducing your breathing for a brief period of 15-30 seconds. Take a rest for a minute and repeat again. Practice this 5-10 times throughout the day to help your body get used to the feeling of a slight air hunger. It's important to note that experiencing air hunger while relaxing should not create tension. If the air shortage is too much, tension will be created. If you find this happening, take a rest from the exercise for 15-30 seconds before commencing again.

In addition, don't be disheartened if your progress is not as quick as you would like. Often, persons with anxiety have perfectionist tendencies. They set high standards for themselves and, in their effort to strive for perfection, they get upset if progress is not according to their liking.

Breathing is a beautiful ingredient of life that should be gently coaxed instead of forced into place. I can assure you that you will make progress as long as you understand the concept of reduced breathing and are able to put it into practice. However, progress does not always occur in a straight line.

If you find reduced breathing while doing sitting exercises too difficult, begin with exercises that involve distraction, such as walking with your mouth closed, any of the small breath hold exercises or bringing your attention to your inner body. These are explained in detail further on.

Important: Guidelines

The breathing exercises in this book are very safe for most people. However, for some people certain precautions are necessary. If you are unsure of your ability, do not attempt any of the breathing exercises without seeking advice from your doctor or Buteyko Clinic practitioner.

Category 1: Only practice nasal breathing, walking with mouth closed and relaxation if you suffer from any of the following conditions:

» Type 1 diabetes (as reduced breathing can lower blood sugar levels, it is important to monitor more frequently)

» Epilepsy

» Schizophrenia

» Chest pains

» Sickle cell anaemia

» Arterial aneurysm

» Any heart problems in the past six months

» Uncontrolled hyperthyroidism

» Cancer

» Kidney disease

Relaxation mp3 file can be downloaded free of charge from: ButeykoClinic.com/123.php

Category 2: If you have any of the following conditions, practice gentle reduced breathing or many small breath holds so long as only a mild feeling of air shortage is experienced:

» Severe asthma

» Emphysema

» COPD

» Type 2 diabetics

» High blood pressure

» Pregnancy (do not practice reduced breathing during the first trimester)

» Anxiety/depression

» Migraine

If you are in **Category 1 or 2** you should make sure that you never create an air shortage greater than what you might normally feel during a gentle walk. An even better option would be to find an experienced practitioner to help formulate a program tailored to your needs and abilities. A list of practitioners can be found at ButeykoClinic.com.

If you are predisposed to anxiety or migraines it's best to increase your CP gently. If your CP increases too quickly you may experience a temporary aggravation of your symptoms. This is only for a short duration and your CP will continue to increase when it passes.

Detoxification

Some people who practice reduced breathing exercises will experience a detoxification. A better breathing volume improves blood flow and oxygenation of tissues and organs. In general, it is a mild aggravation of your symptoms, and can last from several hours to a couple of days.

Typical symptoms include:

- » Increased secretion of mucus from the lungs
- » A head cold with a runny nose
- » Diarrhoea
- » Loss of appetite
- » Increased yawning and fatigue
- » Insomnia
- » Short term headache
- » Increased irritability or anxiety
- » Metallic or coppery taste in the mouth
- » Increased thirst

At most, you are likely to experience only one or two symptoms. An integral part of the detoxification is a reduced appetite for food, therefore only eat when hungry. If you do have a strong reaction, it means your body is undergoing a major physiological change and you will feel much better as a result.

To help reduce the intensity and duration of a detoxification, drink warm water regularly throughout the day and continue with reduced breathing with relaxation. During the detoxification your Control Pause will reduce. Be assured that it will normalise again when the detoxification has passed.

Whether you experience a detoxification or not, by reducing your breathing volume you will soon begin to notice significant signs of health improvement, including:

- » Increased calmness
- » Improved concentration
- » Reduced anxiety
- » Reduced stress
- » More control over thoughts
- » Improved mood
- » Deeper sleep
- » Greater energy
- » Improved well being

Cleansing Reactions

By intensively applying reduced breathing, you will make quicker progress but may experience a stronger cleansing reaction.

By gently applying reduced breathing, you will make slower progress but will experience a more gentle cleansing reaction.

Cleansing reactions are an aggravation of your symptoms. During cleansing, you may experience anxiety, depression, emotions, a racing mind, fatigue, headaches, tummy upset, insomnia, a runny nose and more.

Having a cleansing reaction is not negative. It is positive as your body is becoming healthier. For the first time in your life, you are dealing with the root cause of your condition.

Work your way through the cleansing. It's not easy, but boy is it worth the effort!

Historical symptoms in reverse

As your CP increases, you may experience symptoms in reverse.

As your health condition improves, your immune system frees up to focus on dormant conditions.

Historical health issues can come to the surface for a little while, until your immune system deals with them.

Your health is not getting worse. You are now getting better.

How to stop panic attacks, anxiety and stress with Many Small Breath Holds

(A free video of this exercise is available from www.ButeykoClinic.com.)

This exercise is very useful to stop panic and anxiety attacks and stress. It will produce results similar to the old brown paper bag routine but is a lot safer, as it allows you to maintain your oxygen levels. The objective of this exercise is to keep your breathing calm.

In addition to stopping attacks, Many Small Breath Holds can be practiced hundreds of times per day. If you feel that you are not making progress with reduced breathing exercises, then I encourage you to practice this exercise all day and into the night. It is gentle, suits everybody and will dramatically reduce your symptoms. If you panic while practising any of the remaining reduced breathing exercises, you will find that beginning with this exercise is easier.

Many Small Breath Holds to reduce symptoms:

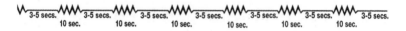

Do *Many Small Breath Holds* of three to five seconds each, as follows.

>> Breathe in, breathe out and hold your breath.

>> Hold your breath for three to five seconds. Do not attempt to hold your breath for longer than this, as this will only increase your breathing and possibly aggravate your symptoms. Your maximum breath hold should be no greater than half your Control Pause at

46

that time. For example, if your CP is four seconds, then do small breath hold for only two seconds.

» After each breath hold, breathe normally for 10 to 15 seconds. Don't interfere with your breathing.

» Continue to do a small breath hold followed by normal breathing for 10 to 15 seconds until your symptoms have passed.

» When you experience the first symptoms of a panic attack, anxiety or stress, immediately do Many Small Breath Holds. Don't wait until the symptoms worsen, as getting your breath under control will be a lot more difficult. If you wake up during the night with attacks, then sit up in bed and do Many Small Breath Holds to calm your breathing.

Very important: these techniques are to be used in conjunction with normal day-to-day treatments.

Nasal Breathing for good health

(A free video of this exercise is available from www.ButeykoClinic.com.)

All of your breathing should only be through your nose. Do not breathe through your mouth. Nature has provided us with a wonderful instrument, our nose, to help make our breathing more regular, filter incoming air and help retain moisture in the body. Many humans sleep, walk, rest and work with their mouth open, as if their nose is nothing more than an ornament!

Mouth breathing generates chaotic and upper chest breathing that stimulates the bodies stress response- the sympathetic nervous system. On the other hand, nasal breathing and correct posture help promote regular and diaphragmatic breathing, thus generating calmness. Just watch a healthy baby breathe for an example of good breathing.

Note:

This exercise creates a medium to large air shortage. If your CP is less than 10 seconds or you have any of the conditions as listed on page 41 then you should refrain from holding your breath for too long and may wish to avoid this exercise. Instead, practice **Many Small Breath Holds** to help unblock your nose and gently relax your breathing.

Your nose gets blocked as a result of breathing too much. Blood vessels become inflamed and larger amounts of mucus are secreted, making breathing through your nose more difficult.

A vicious circle ensues because, as your nose becomes blocked, you switch to mouth breathing. This involves an even greater loss of CO_2, resulting in even more congestion.

The following exercise is very effective for decongesting your nose in just a few minutes.

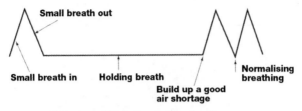

How to unblock the nose naturally

» Sit up straight.

» Take a small breath in through your nose if possible, and a small breath out. If your nose is quite blocked, take a tiny breath in through the corner of your mouth.

» Pinch your nose with your fingers and hold your breath. Keep your mouth closed.

» Gently nod your head or sway your body until you feel that you cannot hold your breath any longer. Hold your nose until you feel a strong desire to breathe.

» When you need to inhale, let go of your nose and breathe gently through it, in and out, with your mouth closed.

» Calm your breathing as soon as possible.

If your nose does not become totally unblocked, wait about 30 seconds until your breathing has recovered before performing this exercise again. You will need to do this exercise a number of times before your nose is completely unblocked.

Doing this exercise many times will unblock your nose. You might also feel warm and more alert given the dilatation of your blood vessels. This exercise is also useful for shifting mucus from the airways and for removing constipation. To

remove constipation, perform this breath hold exercise many times while sitting on the loo!

A low CP indicates that you are breathing big, and your nose will become blocked again. Your nose will remain clear only when your morning CP is over 20 seconds.

Perform this exercise each time that your nose becomes blocked. Even if you have a cold, make sure to breathe through your nose. You might think that you cannot clear your nose when you have a heavy cold, but you can. If you do have a head cold, close your mouth and reduce your breathing throughout the day.

Your nostrils are smaller and thus create more resistance than breathing through your mouth. As a result, you may feel that you are not getting enough air. This sensation will last for a short time. In a few days, your respiratory centre will become accustomed to the more correct volume that you are breathing.

Whatever you do, keep your mouth closed. Your body may begin to play tricks and convince you to breathe more by inducing yawning, sighing, regular sniffing or the odd mouth breath. Do not increase your breathing at this point.

When you feel a need to breathe big arises, for example during a sigh, swallow immediately. If you need to yawn, avoid taking the big breath that accompanies a yawn. Instead, stifle the yawn by keeping your mouth closed or by swallowing.

It takes just a few days for a habitual mouth breather to change into a permanent nasal breather. Increased observation of your breathing and practicing to breathe less are important elements to making this change. Nasal breathing should be enshrined at all times and during every activity. Remember that when you mouth breathe for periods of time, you are reducing oxygenation of your brain!

Correcting breathing volume (easy approach)

There are two approaches to learning how to return your breathing volume to normal levels. The following is the easier version.

Little air shortage

Normal breathing volume

Breathe as normal at end of exercise

Creating a little air shortage

» Sit up straight.

» Bring your attention to your breathing.

» Concentrate on the air flowing into and from your nostrils. Feel the air going in and coming out of the nose. Watch, feel and listen to this for a few minutes.

» Can you feel the air? You might feel cold air on the inner part of your nostrils as it enters your body. You might feel warm air leaving your nostrils.

» You might feel the air moving over the top of your lip.

» Just follow your breath. If a thought comes in, as it will, just bring your attention back to the air passing through your nostrils.

» Keep bringing your attention back to your breath, over and over again. Don't get upset if your mind wanders. This will happen and is the nature of thought. Keep bringing your attention back to your nostrils, over and over again.

When you notice your mind wandering, you are waking up. Before this, you might not have noticed. You might not have known what thoughts you were thinking. You might not have known the effect from these thoughts.

After a few minutes, proceed to the next stage.

» Relax. Imagine tension dissolving from your chest and tummy while you reduce your breathing. As you relax, your breathing will reduce automatically.

» When you can follow your breathing, place your finger under your nose in a horizontal position. Your finger should lie just above your top lip, close enough to your nostrils so that you can feel the air flowing but not so close that you block the air flow.

» Monitor the amount of air flowing through your nostrils.

» Now, breathe air slightly into the tip of your nostrils. For example, just take in enough air to fill your nostrils and no more. Breathe in a flicker of air (maybe 1 cm) with each breath.

» As you exhale, pretend that your finger is a feather. Breathe out gently onto your finger so that the feather does not move.

» When you breathe out, the more warm air you feel, the bigger you are breathing. Concentrate on calming your breath to reduce the amount of warm air you feel on your finger.

» As you reduce the amount of warm air onto your finger, you begin to feel a need or want for air.

» Maintain the need for air for about four minutes. It should be distinct without being stressful.

» You are taking in a small breath (1 cm) and allowing out a relaxed breath. The overall movements of your breathing should have reduced by about 30% to 40%. Minimise the movement of your chest and tummy.

> The need for air during this exercise should be no greater than at the end of the Control Pause.

Another way to describe the feeling you want is that it is like the same level of breathlessness that you feel during a mild walk. The only difference now is that you are sitting still. Knowing this will help reduce any panicky feelings that you may experience. Your need for air should be distinct but not stressful. If your need for air is not distinct, then further reduce your breathing. If your need for air is too stressful, then breathe a little more and allow your body to relax.

If you feel that you cannot grasp this exercise or if you feel too much discomfort, then concentrate on practising Many Small Breath Holds or simply walk with your mouth closed and generate the feeling of needing or wanting air.

As you practice this exercise, you should start to feel warmer as the carbon dioxide increases in your blood. This is good feedback and indicates improved blood flow and oxygenation. If you don't feel warmer, ensure that you have air shortage and that you are able to sustain it for four minutes at a time. Many people also feel their anxiety decrease after commencing this exercise. Their minds become sharper and their tension eases.

Every now and again, your mind may wander. As soon as you notice this, gently bring your attention back to your breathing and reduce it. Since this can happen every five or ten seconds, don't give out to yourself if it is frequent. Your ability to keep your attention on your breathing will greatly improve with practice.

Feel a tolerable but distinct need for air throughout the four minutes. **In addition to improved oxygenation, each time you bring your attention back to your breath you are helping to tame your mind. You are dissolving your thought patterns and the more you watch your breath throughout the day, the more your mind quietens and stillness takes over.**

Correcting breathing volume (a more detailed approach)

The following exercise is the essence of the Buteyko Method. Based on feedback from people attending my clinic, I have also merged the concept of diaphragmatic breathing into this exercise. This is back-to-basics learning to correct the volume and use our diaphragm. This is how we should be breathing every minute, every hour, every day.

There are two parts to this exercise. If you feel that you cannot master this exercise, practice the easier version instead. In time, as your CP increases, you can return to this exercise.

Part 1. Learning to tummy breathe.

Part 2. Bringing reduced and diaphragmatic breathing together.

Since food affects your breathing, it is best to practice this exercise on an empty stomach or at least not straight after eating.

This is by far the most important exercise, as it trains you to be aware of your breathing volume, to permanently change your CO_2 levels and to relax the muscles involved with respiration.

Adopt a correct but comfortable posture. Correct posture involves sitting up straight with both feet under your chair. Sit in the horse rider position at the edge of the chair with your back straight and your knees lower than your hips.

Correct posture is very important in helping to reduce your breathing. If you are slouched, you will compress your diaphragm, increase the tension that you experience and increase your breathing volume.

For example, the following exercise illustrates just how posture affects our breathing:

- » Bend forward;
- » Feel how you are breathing for a couple of minutes;
- » Sit up;
- » Now feel how you are breathing.

You will find that it is a lot easier to breathe while sitting up.

The diaphragm

The diaphragm is our main breathing muscle. It is a dome-shaped sheet of muscle that separates our thorax, which houses the heart and lungs, from our abdomen, which holds the intestines, stomach, liver and kidneys.

Diaphragmatic breathing is more efficient because the amount of blood flow in the lower lobes of the lungs is greater than in the upper. The fast, shallow breaths of people who chronically hyperventilate results in less oxygen transfer to the blood and a greater loss of CO_2. Fast, shallow breaths also activate the body's stress response- the sympathetic nervous system, and this results in more tension. The good news is that diaphragmatic breathing can be easily learned.

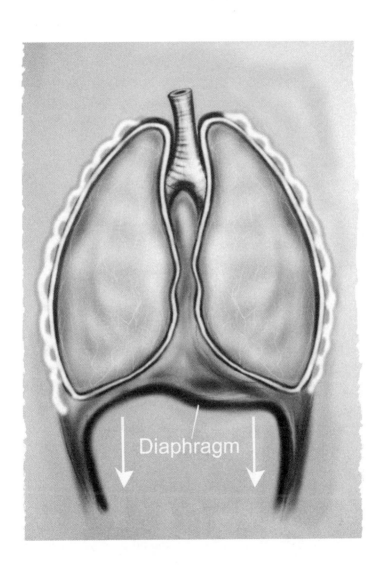

Part 1: learning to tummy breathe

» Place one hand on your chest and the other hand just above your navel.

» As you breathe, allow your shoulders fall to their natural position. Raised or tense shoulders increase the volume of your chest cavity and the volume of air inhaled. Tension increases breathing, while relaxation decreases it.

» With your hand on your chest, exert gentle guidance using your mind and hand to reduce your chest movements.

» At the same time, coordinate your tummy movements with your breathing.

» As you breathe in, gently guide your tummy outwards at the same time. Breathe as if you are breathing into your belly. Do not let your tummy get too big as this might cause dizziness.

» As you breathe out, gently guide your tummy in.

Recap

» Breathe in. Gently guide your tummy out.

» Breathe out. Gently guide your tummy in.

Note that they move in opposite directions from each other. The reason why the tummy moves outwards with an in-breath is because the diaphragm moves downward and exerts gentle force on the abdomen. On the other hand, the tummy moves inward during an exhalation because the diaphragm moves upward and takes pressure from the abdomen.

Part 2: Bringing reduced and diaphragmatic breathing together.

When patients ask me what is more important, I say that reduced breathing is primary and tummy breathing is secondary. At the same time, the two work together as it is a lot easier to reduce breathing volume by changing the breathing pattern to diaphragmatic. To bring the two together:

» Sit up straight, as described above.

» Place one hand on your chest and one hand above your navel.

» Bring attention to your breathing.

» As you breathe in, gently guide your tummy out. Use your mind and awareness to keep your chest movements to a minimum.

» As you breathe out, gently guide your tummy in, again keeping your chest movements quiet.

» As you breathe with your tummy, concentrate on making your in-breath smaller.

» With each breath, take in less air than what you would like to. Make the in-breath smaller or shorter. Apply gentle pressure with your hands against your chest and tummy to create a slight resistance to your breathing. Feel as if you are breathing against your hands.

» Reduce your volume of breathing by encouraging your entire body to relax. As you feel your body relaxing, your breathing will reduce automatically.

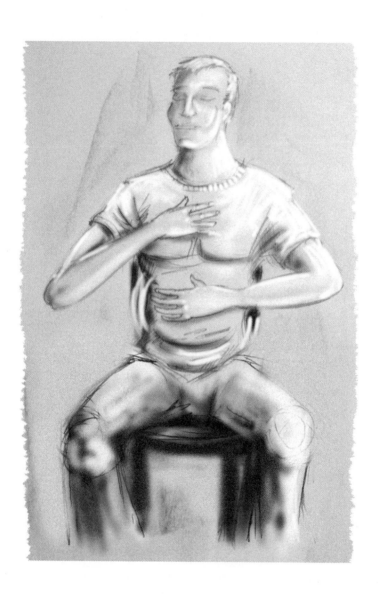

» Breathe out with a relaxed exhalation. While breathing out, allow the natural elasticity of your lungs and diaphragm to play their role in the exhalation. Imagine a balloon slowly deflating by its own accord.

» As your in-breath is smaller and your out-breath is relaxed, visible movements will slow down. Aim to quieten your breathing. A typical session may involve reducing your breathing movement by 30% to 40%.

» If your stomach gets tense, jerky or "hard," then the degree of air shortage is too great. Instead, relax for a moment. When your tension dissolves, return to gentle reduced breathing.

» You must feel a need for air that is tolerable. Maintain this tolerable "air hunger" for three to five minutes at a time.

I am often asked whether a person is doing the exercise properly. The answer to this is:

> **"You are reducing your breathing when you feel a distinct but non-stressful need for air."**

Sometimes, to reinforce this point, I say:

> **"Unless you feel a tolerable need for air, you will not make progress."**

Your need for air should be distinct but not stressful. If your need for air is not distinct, then reduce your movements further. If your need for air is too stressful, then breathe a little more and allow your body to relax.

Now you have mastered relaxing your diaphragm combined with a reduced need for air. Every breath that you take throughout the day should be diaphragmatic and quiet. Remember, this is how we breathed when we were healthy young babies. Our lips were together, and our little tummies moved in and out with each breath. Healthy breathing is all about going back to basics.

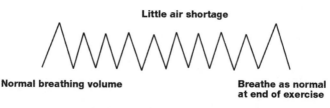

Little air shortage

Normal breathing volume

Breathe as normal at end of exercise

Creating a little air shortage

Anger, anxiety and stress originate from chaotic and fast breathing. In Japan, children are taught from a young age to diaphragmatically breathe and keep their breathing calm when they get angry. When you are under stress, immediately pay attention to your breathing. If you keep your breathing level calm and quiet, stress is less likely to manifest. Stress and anger require heavy and irregular breathing. To observe this, watch your breathing the next time you get stressed or are angry.

Recap

Small breath in. Relaxed breath out.
Small breath in. Relaxed breath out.
Small breath in. Relaxed breath out.

A small breath simply means taking a smaller or shorter breath than what you would normally take. A relaxed breath out tends to be slow.

Don't worry too much about your rate. Ideally, it should not increase but it may when your CP is less than 20 seconds. If your rate increases, calm and slow down your breathing. As your CP increases, your rate will naturally decrease.

Change your breathing from this:

Low CP - 10 seconds

Noisy, loud, big, erratic, irregular, effortful, tense, inefficient breathing.

To this:

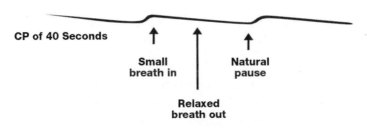

CP of 40 Seconds

Small breath in

Relaxed breath out

Natural pause

Quiet, silent, small, level, regular, effortless, relaxed, efficient breathing.

A formal routine for correcting your breathing (easy and detailed approaches)

Worksheets are provided towards the end of book.

- **»** Measure your pulse.

- **»** Take your Control Pause.

- **»** Reduce your breathing for four minutes.

- **»** Wait two minutes and take your Control Pause.

- **»** Reduce your breathing for four minutes.

- **»** Wait two minutes and take your Control Pause.

- **»** Reduce your breathing for four minutes.

- **»** Wait two minutes and take your Control Pause.

- **»** Reduce your breathing for four minutes.

- **»** Wait two minutes and take your Control Pause.

- **»** Measure your pulse.

Your CP taken at the end of the four sets should be about 25% higher than the one taken at the start.

Your pulse as measured at the end of the 20 minutes should be a couple of beats per minute lower than your pulse measured at the start. If your pulse is higher, then rest for a few minutes and re-measure. If it is still high, then this is a sign that you were stressed during the exercise. The next time you practice, ensure that you experience a shortage of air but place more emphasis on relaxation.

The normal resting pulse for an adult should be between 60 and 80 beats per minute. A child's pulse will be higher than this and will decrease as he or she gets older.

Twenty to thirty minutes first thing in the morning is an excellent way to reverse the heavy breathing from the night before. Repeat the same process during the day and as the last thing that you do at night. Reducing your breathing before going to bed will ensure a calm and restful sleep and will give you very good energy levels when you wake in the morning.

> While doing your four sets of four minutes, experience an air shortage for the <u>entire four minutes.</u>
> Reducing your breathing for the first 30 seconds and then breathing heavily for the remaining three and a half minutes is not useful.

You might find it difficult to set aside twenty minutes three times a day; do your best. Know that every minute of reduced breathing is also a minute that you give your mind to rest from its normal activity. Your mind also needs a rest from its incessant and repetitive thoughts. Watching, feeling and reducing your breath creates quiet time for your mind.

(Please note: To assist with continuous relaxation, the enclosed CD is slightly different to the above approach as it runs without any interruptions)

Informal routine for correcting your breathing volume (easy and detailed approach)

If you feel that you can practice reduced breathing as part of your daily life, then reduce your breathing and create an air shortage for blocks of about four or five minutes several times throughout the day.

Reducing your breathing for 90 minutes throughout the day helps restore your breathing volume to normal levels. This is easier done than you may think. If you like walking, then breathe through your nose and reduce your breathing for the entire walk. If you like to meditate, reduce your breathing during meditation. If you like to drive, reduce your breathing while driving. If you watch TV or read, reduce your breathing while doing these activities. If you work on a computer, reduce your breathing. Placing your finger under your nose to reduce your breathing is not a requirement. All that is required is that you relax your chest and diaphragm and breathe less than what you normally do.

> You are breathing less when you feel a tolerable air shortage. Sustain this feeling for blocks of four minutes several times throughout the day (informally) or during four four-minute blocks (formally).

If your tummy gets tense or jumpy, then your air shortage is too great and can create tension. If this happens, distract yourself for a few seconds and return to gentle reduced breathing.

With practice, your breathing will become calm, quiet and still. Your other option is to continue with the heavy breathing, have all of your attention in your head and deprive your brain of oxygen, resulting in increased thought activity.

Reduced breathing serves two purposes: the first is to improve oxygenation of the brain and the second is to take attention away from the head and to the body. Both together are powerful tools for reducing thought activity and anxiety.

Bringing reduced breathing into your way of life

I am sitting in a cafe in Spiddal, Co Galway as I write this. A cup of coffee sits on a wooden table. Music is playing in the background—classical music instead of the usual traditional Irish.

People chat and the coffee machine is percolating. The sun is shining outside.

I sense my breathing, and follow my breath in and out. My breath is quiet and slow. In and out, in and out. I feel my tummy move in and out, very slowly, ever slightly. A gap arises between breaths. A natural gap. Not intentional. I relax my body and feel my breath quietening even further. Slowly slowing, slowing, slowing. A small air shortage occurs. Only a gentle shortage. My tummy is a little tense. Not sure why. I bring my attention to my tummy. New people have just arrived and are shown a seat. I type as I follow my breath. Watching my breath. Feeling my breath. My mind is still, quiet and relaxed. An intense alertness. Watching my breath. Hearing the gentle noise of music, of chatter. Tourists are on their holidays. Somebody talks about not having to pay tax at Shannon. Attention is back to my breath, tension has now dissolved in my tummy. Following my breath. No movement from my chest. My tummy gently moves in and out. Quiet, slow, relaxed, even breaths. A slight air shortage. I continue to feel this slight air shortage. A new customer walks in. The girl serving must know him as she predicts what he is going to drink. She is an attractive Irish girl. I take a drink of the coffee and taste a slight bitterness mixed with the brown sugar. Back to breathing. Back to typing. My mind has no tension. No anxiety. No rushing thoughts. My breathing is quiet, quiet.

CHAPTER 4
Physical exercise to still the mind

To produce more CO_2, move your muscles!

In my experience, persons partaking in regular physical exercise have better control of their stress and anxiety than those who don't.

This section is about exercising safely and getting the maximum benefits from it.

The importance of exercise

There are only two ways to increase CO_2 in the human organism. The first is to reduce breathing volume and the second is to produce more CO_2 by engaging in physical exercise. CO_2 is generated through inner respiration from the process of converting food and oxygen into energy. An exercising muscle generates more CO_2, thus encouraging the release of oxygen from haemoglobin to that muscle. Remember that the presence of CO_2 loosens the bond between oxygen and haemoglobin within red blood cells.

Nasal breathing

A low CP corresponds to greater breathing volume. As a result, never breathe through your mouth if your CP is lower than 20 seconds, as your breathing will be greater than what your body requires. You can open your mouth during sports for short periods when your CP is higher than 20 seconds.

All of your breathing should be through your nose. Initially, this might feel impossible because of an ingrained habit to breathe through your mouth.

But don't worry, as breathing through your nose is easy to master. In the beginning, you might find that you are unable to walk as quickly as you can with your mouth open, as a sense of breathlessness will be more intense. In a few days, this will pass and your walking will steadily improve. It is a case of quality over quantity.

Your breathing volume will increase during exercise. This is not a problem when there is a reasonable match with your metabolic requirements. However, the lower your CP, the poorer the match; hence, the need to control your breathing.

Feel the need for air and do enough exercise to create a sweat

To get the most benefit from physical activity, feel a need for air. In other words, get to a point where you are breathless. Ideally, spend enough time doing physical exercise to produce a sweat. Walking at a good pace with your mouth closed for a half an hour to one hour is great exercise.

When your CP is low, it is very easy to disrupt your breathing so be careful. Go gently and don't push yourself beyond the point that you cannot control your breathing. At the same time, feel a tolerable need for air.

Exercise provides three ways to create your need for air:

1. Go faster with your mouth closed;
2. Breathe less during exercise;
3. Practice breath holds during exercise (explained in detail further on).

If your need for air is so great that you need to open your mouth, slow down and calm your breathing. You recover faster if you keep your mouth closed. If you are walking for exercise, walk alone or agree with your walking partner to not talk. Talking will only undo the benefits of exercise.

Feel relaxed throughout

As you commence your physical exercise, alternate your attention between your breathing and your inner body. Exercise is your time, so don't spend it worrying about problems.

For the half hour, make a commitment to yourself to bring your attention to your breath or body over and over again.

Each day, I try to get out for one hour of exercise. I thrive on it and if I cannot do it because of rainy weather, I feel like I missed something from my day.

As I walk, I bring attention to my breath. I follow my breath and breathe diaphragmatically. I sense the area around my tummy. If it is tense, I bring attention to it and encourage it to relax. Any tension will dissolve with a little imagination and mental encouragement. I bring attention to my breath. I follow my breath. Is it quick? Is it easy? Is it fast? Is it hard? Is there a need for air? Is there no need for air? I follow my breath. I don't analyse it. I just sense it.

At first, my breath is relatively quiet. I walk for the first ten minutes to accumulate carbon dioxide before I increase my pace. This helps keep my breathing calm as I move to a jog. During my jog, I just follow my breath, keep my attention on my inner body and feel relaxed. It is wonderful to bring attention from your head and into the body.

After ten minutes, I increase my pace to a jog. I keep my mouth closed for the entire duration of my jog. I continue to watch my breath and feel my inner body. I can feel slight vibrations rising through my body as I take each step. At the same time, I try to completely relax my tummy. Sometimes, thoughts enter. I keep an eye out for them and, as soon as they enter, I bring attention back to my breath.

This type of physical exercise is a form of meditation and is a great opportunity to take attention from my mind and bring it to the inner body. In addition, because I push my body a little, my mind activity stops. After a few minutes, I can feel the high from exercise. My body is warm and sweating, my breathing is faster and my head is clear. Because I keep my mouth closed throughout my jog, my breathing recovers quickly.

No matter what exercise you do, watch your breath and feel your inner body. Repeat to the tension around your tummy: relax, relax, relax.

How to determine if you are breathing correctly during physical exercise

Measure your CP before exercise;

Perform physical exercise;

Measure your CP 15–30 minutes after you have completed your exercise.

Your CP measurement 15 minutes after exercise should be greater than your CP measurement before exercise.

Bear in mind two points:

1. If your CP is measured immediately after exercise, it will probably be lower than your starting CP because of the existing air shortage.

2. If 30 minutes after exercise your CP is still lower than your starting CP, you were breathing excessively during exercise.

People who exercise are more relaxed

Stress reflects changes in our body primarily to help us. When we are stressed, the fight or flight response has been activated and our body is programmed for physical activity. To release this activation, go out for a walk or a jog or whatever exercise you enjoy. If you are unable to remove yourself from your environment, control your breathing and, later that day, ensure to get physical activity.

Those who exercise regularly are calmer and more productive than their colleagues. Exercise enables quicker recovery after activation of the fight or flight response. Chemicals that are released are removed quicker and your body's systems can return to their normal operating rates. Exercise also releases pent-up negative energy, enhances self-esteem and is a useful tool to use to escape from work and other commitments.

The following is a summary of the key points regarding physical exercise:

1. It is absolutely essential to do physical exercise.

2. Exercise within your capabilities.

3. Never breathe through your mouth during exercise if your CP is less than 20 seconds.

4. The lower your CP, the more careful you should be while performing physical exercise.

5. Feel the need for air during physical exercise.

6. Perform thirty minutes to one hour of physical exercise per day.

7. Make sure to go gently with your mouth closed for the first 10 minutes.

8. Make sure to calm your breathing immediately following exercise.

9. Walk, don't talk.

Breath hold during exercise

This exercise involves holding your breath on the out-breath while engaging in any physical activity. You can do this while walking, skipping, using a trampoline, cycling, etc.

This is a very effective exercise for ensuring that your breathing is reduced, calm and gentle during the day. The length of time of your breath hold depends on the state of your health and your CP.

5-20 Steps   1/2 min.   5-20 Steps   1/2 min.   5-20 Steps   1/2 min.   5-20 Steps

» While walking breathe in, breathe out and hold your breath

» Walk 5 to 20 paces with your breath held

» Resume breathing and continue to walk

» After 30 seconds to 1 minute of walking with normal breathing, repeat breath hold as above

» Repeat small breath hold every half minute to one minute

» Ensure that your inner body is relaxed throughout

» If there is tension in your tummy or chest, encourage this area to relax

Maintain control of your breathing throughout

There is no hard and fast rule as to how many times you do this. The more often you perform breath holds throughout the day, the better. The objective with any exercise is to produce a sweat and feel warmer. This exercise is far better than walking alone, as it creates a slightly higher air shortage.

If you do experience a light headache while walking with breath holds, don't be concerned. This is a good sign and indicates increased CO_2 levels. Your headache will soon dissipate and you will feel better.

CHAPTER 5
Further stilling
the mind

Meditation is simply stilling and relaxing the mind.

Focusing on the breath, feeling the inner body and occupying the senses is meditation.

Connect with the inner body

Placing attention on the inner body is a truly wonderful thing to do. Western man rarely places attention on the inner body unless he is in pain. Seldom does he have his attention on the body when it is free from pain. Seldom does he experience the vibration of energy that resonates there. The body is your connection with life itself. Your body is life.

If you have never placed attention on your body before, start off slowly. If you have already been following and reducing your breath, you will find this relatively easy to do.

Close your eyes and bring attention to one of your hands. Feel your hand from within. Stay with the energy field of your hand for a little while. When you have a good feeling of the inner energy field of your hand, move your attention to include your arm. Now feel the energy field of your hand and arm together. Don't analyse or think about it, just feel it.

Next, bring attention to your chest and feel it from within for a couple of minutes. Then bring attention to your stomach. Feel whether there is any tension here. If your stomach is tense, imagine it gradually relaxing. Feel the area around your tummy relaxing by itself. Feel the tension dissolving. The more active your mind, the greater the tendency for your stomach to be in a knot. Relax this area using your imagination.

Now feel the energy field of both hands, both arms, your chest and your tummy at the same time. Keep your attention there. Your body will rejoice in the attention that you are giving it. As long as your attention is on your body, it is not on your mind. The incessant thought activity of your mind has stopped.

When you are focusing on reducing your breathing, you are out of your mind. You are giving your chatter a rest. Wonderful!

When you have attention on your inner body, you are out of your mind. You are taking back ownership of your mind.

When your complete attention is on your senses, you are out of your mind. You did this naturally as a child.

You cannot have complete attention on your inner body and at the same time have mental noise. With a little practice, you will be able to feel your entire body from head to toe.

During the day as you go about your daily affairs, bring attention to your breathing and your inner body. As you drive your car, have 70% of your attention on driving and 30% in your inner body. As you walk, feel your body relax throughout.

As you watch TV, don't surrender all of your attention to the TV, but immerse yourself in your inner body. If there is confrontation on TV, bring attention immediately to your inner body. Don't become absorbed with the tension, stress, anger and fighting that takes place on popular soap operas. Better still, don't watch them at all. The popularity of such soaps is an indication of our mad world. As you relate to your children, friends, family or any person, listen to them with your entire body. Feel your body as you listen. This is real listening.

As you brush your teeth, feel your inner body. As you sit on the toilet, feel your inner body. As you queue up at the post office, feel your inner body. If you are stressed, feel your inner body. As you do a boring job, take attention into your body and don't just think about how much you hate your job. As you walk, feel your inner body. As you empty the dishwasher, feel your inner body.

As you eat, taste the food and feel your inner body. Stay in your body. As you lie in bed at night, feel your inner body. This is not just something that you do every now and again. This is something that you reside in permanently. Every minute, every hour, every day, take attention out of your head and your story and merge yourself with the body.

You still have use of your mind whenever you need it for a practical situation. However, you will have reduced the meaningless and devastating habit of repetitive thinking. The inner body has an intelligence far greater than just a collection of thoughts. Merge with that intelligence. Don't avoid it all the time by living in your head.

As long as attention is on your inner body, your mind is calm. If for a moment you forget about keeping attention on your inner body, then you are back in your mind. This will happen quite often at the start. Don't start giving out to yourself if you find it difficult to place your attention on your inner body for more than a few minutes. This is simply the habit of an active mind. To change this habit, keep bringing attention to your inner body. If your mind wanders again, keep bringing it back. The more you practice this, the better and easier it gets.

Your mind activity is your choice. Do you want to keep repeating the insane nonsense running through your head or do you want to connect with life? Bring attention home to your body.

As you become proficient with awareness of your inner body, incorporate gentle, reduced breathing through relaxation. While relaxed, allow your breathing to calm by itself. Feel a tolerable but comfortable need for air. Feel your inner body. Feel your tummy gently move with each breath.

Are you connected to the wonders of life ?

Most of us are blessed with the traditional five senses of sight, hearing, touch, smell and taste. A sixth sense is intuition, which is to sense something in advance or to know what course of action to take based on a feeling or a hunch instead of logical processing.

Our five senses enable us to directly experience life on earth. How often do you use your five senses with an undivided mind?

When we put our total attention on our five senses, we are out of our mind and are connecting with reality. When you look, look. When you touch, touch. When you taste, taste. When you smell, smell. While using your senses, have nothing else running through your mind. Just be there with your full attention. Set aside the activity of your mind and merge with your surroundings.

The question is how much time do you spend using your five senses without the mental commentary running in the background? Is your complete attention regularly on the five senses or is some of it on your senses, with the remainder in your head? When you look, do you really see unhindered by thought? Are you seeing, or is there mental commentary perceiving, analysing and labelling what you are seeing? When you hear, are you listening with all of your attention? Or is there part listening and part mental noise? When you smell, do you really smell with all of your attention, or is your attention divided? When you taste, do you really taste? How much of you is really involved with the tasting?

Watch how children relate to life. Their heads are not full of thoughts. See the clarity and transparency of the eyes of a child. You can literally look through them. Be like a child. Go back to the innocence and wonder of childhood when everything was fresh, new and exhilarating.

The wonder of nature disappears when an adult starts to teach a child: this is a tree, this is a flower, that is a dog, that is a cow, there is a horse, that is grass, the grass is green. No longer do children see and feel the aliveness from the tree or the horse, or grass or nature. Instead, they now have a word for these tangible objects. It is a tree. It is a horse. It is a dog. It is reduced to a label, a name. The sensitivity of what is behind the name has gone forever. The child is beginning to go to sleep.

Let the child know the name of the horse. Also help the child sense the aliveness of what is behind the word. Life is dull when nature is nothing more than a few names.

Is your attention in your head all the time or are you connected with what is going on around you? Make it a habit throughout the day to use your senses. As you go for a walk or a drive, don't be on autopilot. Look with your eyes, hear with your ears, feel with your inner and outer body. Connect with life and take your attention out of your head. Do this many, many times throughout the day.

Your job on earth is to live life. You are living life when you are connecting directly to it and not living in a collection of thoughts.

Going for a walk but missing out on everything

You take a walk in the park. Vivid colours surround you: green grass, blue sky, brightly coloured flowers. The sun radiates on your shoulders and neck. Children are chatting, shouting and laughing in delight. A dog barks in excitement in the distance.

You walk through the park and running through your head is what you are going to have for dinner tonight, the shopping list that you have prepared, whether you have written everything down or maybe you have forgotten an item, what time to collect Ciara from school, you hope that the traffic later is not too bad, yesterday the traffic was dreadful and you felt stressed when you collected Ciara as you thought that you were late picking her up, the weather did not help yesterday, it was cold and you were concerned that the child was getting cold, but today the weather is nice and that won't be a problem, what will I have for dinner, maybe I will try a new menu, but are there enough potatoes for that dish? Is the sauce in the cupboard or did I write it on the shopping list? Have I brought my card to pay for the shopping? Oh, the cost of food these days, it was never like that before. Well, at least I am doing some exercise. I meant to exercise more but it is difficult to find the time. What time is it? Oh, yes, that's the time. I'd better rush to collect Ciara, jump into the car, get stuck in traffic. Why is the traffic like this? Every car just has one person sitting in it. So much for the policymakers, the roads cannot hold the traffic. In Ireland, the roads are just too narrow. Why don't we have roads like in they have in USA? What is this idiot doing in front of me? Go on, will you? Why are you driving slowly? Honk honk.

That is life for most people. They take a walk and miss everything around them. Where was their attention? More importantly, where is your attention?

Taking ownership of the mind

It is worth spending some time where there is innate stillness. Nature provides this in abundance.

I like to stare into open space. I am fortunate enough to have miles of untouched bog land in the front of where I live. I have been looking and merging with this for a number of years, yet each time feels like the first. Because I set aside my mind and put my entire attention on it, I become one with it.

No matter how many times a day I look, there is a newness, a freshness and an aliveness. I am not looking at the countryside through thoughts, through labels, through names. I get so much more when I truly look. Nature is constantly changing, dying and renewing. Therefore, each time I look without the filter of my mind, the landscape has changed from before. A river that flows is not the same river five minutes later. Nor is it the same river five minutes before. The water is different. One pheasant is not the same as the next. Humans might attach the same label by calling it a pheasant, but each is unique, beautiful and individual.

The essence of nature is not understood through thought. Truly appreciating nature does not come through the amount of information or the names you attach to different flowers, birds or animals. You are not going into nature to exercise your mind. Instead, go into nature to give your mind a rest. Who cares about the name of the tree or the bird? Instead, just look at the tree or bird without thought and sense its aliveness. This is far more important than knowing a mere label.

If you have great difficulty doing this and your mind continues to bombard you with thought, then take this process little by little. In addition to stilling your mind through nature, watch your breath and pay attention to your inner body. Feel your body from the inside. Be connected with it. Feel your body as you merge with the life around you. Life takes care of the flowers, grass, trees and birds. There is nothing wanting here. Nature is immersed in stillness and will help take you there too. You have nothing to do but to stop thinking.

Simple things that life has to offer

Write down sixty things that you love to do. Write down things that totally absorb your mind to the point of excluding all else. List anything, with the exception of taking alcohol and drugs, that absorbs your attention to the point of self-forgetfulness.

At first, you might feel that drawing up such a list is impossible. But upon closer examination, you will be very surprised at how many items you can write down. What would you do to be totally engrossed to the point that nothing else comes into your mind?

Be grateful for what you have. Appreciate what you have. When you are having a bad day and you find it a little trifling to still your mind, choose an item or two from the list and spend time doing it. This will reduce the activity in your mind and you will be in a better place afterwards to deal with the issue. You will also realise that the simple things in life are provided in abundance and they give us the most pleasure. These are things like:

» Sitting in a nice cafe with a good cup of coffee

» Going for a drive in the country

» Going to the gym

» Spending time in Galway

» Spending time with Sinead

» Meditating

» Reading self-help books

» Writing

» Settling down my thoughts

» Focusing on my breath

» Going for a snooze under a warm duvet

» Sitting in the sun

» Walking in nature

» Playing with the kids

» Watching a good movie

» Meeting with friends

» Going for a nice meal

» Stilling the mind in nature

Refer to your list and do a couple of things from it when you are feeling down.

The number of times you

bring attention to your

inner body throughout the

day is more important than

the length of time that you

hold your attention during

one sitting.

CHAPTER 6
How to have a great night's sleep

For good health, NEVER breathe through your mouth at night.

A lower CP reflecting larger breathing volume will result in many of the symptoms below. How many do you experience?

- » Snoring
- » Sleep apnoea (holding your breath many times throughout the night)
- » Disrupted sleep
- » Sweating
- » Racing mind
- » Nightmares
- » Needing to use the bathroom at about 5 am or 6 am
- » Children wetting the bed during the night
- » Fatigue first thing in morning
- » Brain fog upon waking
- » Dry mouth
- » Upper or lower respiratory complaints

Solution:

- » Do not eat anything two hours before going to bed as food increases breathing.
- » A cool bedroom is best (but not cold). It is better to have no central heating in a bedroom and to ensure that your duvet or bedclothes are not excessively warm. High temperatures increase breathing. In addition, an airy bedroom is best.

- Don't sleep on your back. Instead, sleep on your tummy or left hand side. Sleeping on your back is by far the worst position as there is no restriction to your breathing. The tummy is the most preferred position, as the weight of your body against the mattress will automatically help you to breathe less.

- Ensure that your mouth is closed at night.

> To eliminate insomnia, reduce your breathing by relaxing for fifteen minutes before bed. Sit on a chair or in a meditation position. Close your eyes and follow your breathing. Continuously allow your breathing to quieten and relax. Feel a comfortable and tolerable air shortage. This will ensure continued sleep without disruptions.

Closing your mouth at night

We recommend that adults wear a paper tape while sleeping to gently keep their lips together. Paper tape can be bought at most chemists. A good brand is 3M and a suitable size is one inch. Apply it horizontally to cover your mouth. If you are unable to place it in a horizontal position, then place it vertically. Before applying, fold over a tab at either end of the tape to make removal easier in the morning.

Wearing the tape at night is imperative to a good night's sleep and will significantly improve your energy levels upon waking. In fact, all of the symptoms listed above will be reduced if you keep your mouth closed at night. If you have had copious amounts of alcohol, are epileptic or are feeling nauseous, do not wear the tape.

Some people may possibly, and very reasonably, experience panic at the thought of having their mouth taped. To help overcome this, put the tape on your mouth half an hour before going to bed. This should be enough time to allow you to adjust to using the tape and to overcome any nervousness. For the first few nights, wearing the tape will feel a little strange. It may come off during the night, but at least you will have spent some hours breathing through your nose.

Continue to wear the tape until you have managed to change to breathing through your nose at night. How long this takes will vary with the individual. Breathing through your nose will result in a naturally moist mouth when you wake up. If your mouth is dry upon waking, you know that your mouth was open during sleep.

CHAPTER 7
Know thyself

How your thoughts
determine your reality

Each human has an in-built film or memory that stores all of his or her past experiences, events and thoughts. Over thousands of years, society, propaganda, religious beliefs, personal opinions and experiences all contribute to this program. For most humans, their entire life is based on this collection of stored programs. Their behaviour, beliefs, actions, thoughts and words are all pre-determined by the influences of others. In other words, they don't get to live their own lives. They live according to whatever program has been installed.

Think of a movie projector at a cinema. A film is installed into the projector and a light shines through the film to project the picture onto the big screen.

With humans, the light of the projector is our true self and we look through our film of past experiences and our life unfolds according to this script.

A person with a film filled with racism will automatically see every coloured person as inferior without even being conscious of this belief. In areas of the world with continuous fighting among religious groups, individuals in each group fail to see the real person on the other side. They see the person through their film or collection of thoughts. They don't see the life of another person, as they have reduced the person to a label or a word, such as a Hindu or a Muslim or a Christian.

Someone with an inferiority complex will look through thoughts of inadequacy, poor self-esteem, poor confidence and self-criticism. Each time they look in the mirror, they won't like what they see. They see their own life in negative ways based on the thoughts that they have saved onto their film. The more they run the same thoughts through their head, the stronger, sharper and more real is the image that they have of themselves. Eventually, they may come to hate themselves, all as a result of their own imagination and thoughts.

Whatever is stored in the film determines our outlook on life. Good films are better than bad films. However, in any event, any film that we look through is divorced from life. As long as we continue to live on autopilot and through stored films or programs, we are asleep. We are asleep from the moment our analytical mind begins to function at around four years of age, to the moment we die. We are the living dead.

As long as our attention is caught up in our mind, it is divided. Part of our attention is looking through our film of thoughts and the remainder is focused on life.

The objective is to allow our true self to connect directly with life and not through our past thoughts. The objective is to leave aside the film and focus 100% of our attention on life. Past thoughts are in the past; they are stale. They reflect other people's and society's opinions. At best, they are figments of the imagination. They are not life.

Have you ever observed your thoughts? What is watching your thoughts? Who is the real you? Is the real you the watcher or is it the thoughts running through your head?

There cannot be two of you, can there? Who is the observer? Is the observer of thoughts the real you? Is the observer the light in the projector? Or is the real you a collection of thoughts?

I would like you to seriously consider these questions.

"One day this terrible war will be over. The time will come when we will be people again and not just Jews."

— ANNE FRANK (APRIL 11, 1944)

Who is the real you?

The real you is the part of you that can watch your thoughts. It is the observer. It is your awareness. It remains even after this body dies. The real you is constant; it does not change. It is the only part of you that is real. It is sometimes called our soul, true self or higher being. The real you is your consciousness. It is one with all life.

Suffering does not take place in the real you. Suffering only takes place in your mind, but your mind is not you. Your arm is not you. Your leg is not you. Your hand is not you. When our bodies die, our arms, legs and hands cease to function. Life has expired from them. Life will also have expired from your mind. Your mind ceases at death. You cannot think when you are dead. Your mind does not continue to function as you lie in the coffin. The only part of you that continues to function after this body dies is the real you. It is accessed only through a still mind. This is the door to freedom.

It is your mind or your collection of thoughts that determines your suffering. Through thought, your mind creates emotions in the body. In turn, these emotions feed your mind. The more you think about that ass of a boss, or that idiot of a neighbour, or that lousy wife, or that clown of a husband, the more anger builds up in you. This increased anger feeds your mind. Your mind feeds your emotions.

If you were not thinking, if the real you were directly in contact with life, would there be anger? What creates anger? What creates tension?

Our thoughts create our state of mental health; nothing else but our thoughts.

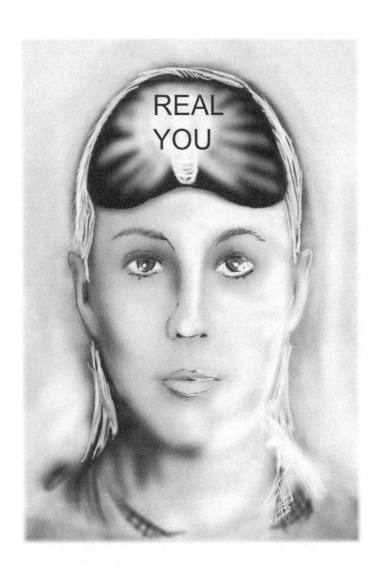

Stay present and connect directly with life instead of doing so through a collection of thoughts, experiences and events. Drop the thoughts. Set them aside not through force but through the realisation that thoughts are not who we are. If the mind is not us, then thoughts originating from the mind are not us.

This is liberating. We understand thought to be just a thought and nothing more. We have the choice to follow it or not. We begin to see thought NOT as truth or something that we must adhere to and blindly follow. We understand thought as a collection of good and not so good influences that we have stored in our film.

With this understanding, you see the film for what it is. The light of your true self can then shine without thought. Only then do you truly live in your natural state. Once you realise this, your life will positively change forever. If this is your first introduction to this concept, stick with it. This is not intellectual debate. This is about understanding your mind, which alone determines your happiness on earth.

113

You are not your mind

Imagine if your right arm never stopped moving. It moves up and down many times a minute. Sometimes the movement is small and sometimes the movement is large. The activity of your right arm is a major hindrance. At the same time, it is indispensible; you are able to instruct and tell it what to do and, generally, it continues to perform any activity that your left arm does.

The only difference is that in between use and while at rest, your right arm continues to move about. Each day, your right arm constantly bumps into things. It accidentally knocks things over and hits other people. Every now and again, it even hits you.

You are not as focused when you drive, or work, rest, meet other people or entertain. In fact, your right arm always needs a part of your attention, no matter what you do. Even if you are listening to somebody talk, the moving right arm is a distraction.

Even though every human has inherited a moving right arm, they still become annoyed when they are at the receiving end of it. They don't seem to realise that both they and you are oblivious that the right arm knocked them and not the real you. You don't mean to knock into people. It just happens.

Some people have completely lost control of their right arm. They spend many hours in a pub drinking alcohol in an effort to tranquilize it. The next day, when the alcohol wears off, the right arm moves twice as fast as it normally does. Others run to a doctor, who prescribes drugs to calm the right arm.

A few other unfortunates feel so much pain from the right arm that this same arm eventually becomes the instrument that takes their lives. These poor people died by their own right hand.

Every human has this moving right arm, with the exception of a few who have realised that it is a tool that can be tamed, and that with attention you can control your right arm. You have inherited this right arm as a condition from humankind. Over the millennia, the right arm has developed a bad habit. It is slightly flawed. It simply does not stop moving.

At some point, you realise that you can control your right arm. You realise that you are not your right arm. Even though it is part of your body on Earth, it is not you. The real you, your true self, can observe the antics of the right arm. The real you watches your right arm and begins to observe its movement. The more frequently the real you watches your right arm, the more you will see its habits. You begin to see the triggers that cause it to move quicker. You begin to notice that the more the arm moves, the more it feeds itself and continues to move.

With this realisation, through alertness you keep your right arm still. When you are ready, your right arm becomes more under your control. You are able to connect with life and what goes on around you without your right arm moving incessantly. A moving right arm is no longer a distraction that took your attention from anything that you tried to apply yourself to.

There is little difference between a moving right arm and the human mind. The main difference is that it is easy to identify the right arm. The arm is external, visible and can be readily noticed. The human mind is cleverly located to avoid detection. It is hidden away from view and carries on unhindered in the background.

We have lost our ability to control our minds. Our minds move incessantly in the background. Recognise your mind as a moving right arm.

Watch your thoughts

When you are asleep in life, thoughts completely take you over. You fail to differentiate between who you really are and the thoughts that take place in your mind. You accept your thoughts as totally true and blindly react to them.

For most people, their thoughts are in the background. They are a constant drone of noise that they are completely unaware of.

As we awake, we realise the distinction between the thoughts of our mind and who we truly are. Our true self is peace, happiness and pure joy. It is the out-of-control mind that creates suffering, agitation and misery.

To begin this process, watch your thoughts. Be a good gardener of your mind. Be attentive to what is growing in your mind, just as a good gardener is aware of the weeds that are trying to take hold while at the same time nurturing the flowers. Turn up the volume of your thoughts. Bring them to the surface. Observe them.

I'm not talking about thoughts that we need to deal with a practical situation. Instead, I'm taking about the background noise in your head as you perform certain activities or routines throughout the day.

Keep an eye on repetitive thoughts. What thoughts do you repeat over and over again? How long have you been running these thoughts through your head? When do your thoughts arise most frequently? What affect do these thoughts have on your body? How do you feel when you think these thoughts? Do you reach a conclusion from these thoughts? Do they help you in any way? How much time do these thoughts take from you?

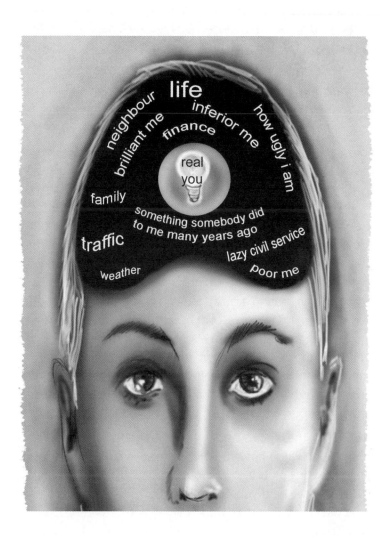

119

Don't analyse your thoughts, as I don't wish to replace one form of thought with another. I just want you to notice your thoughts, how often they occur and how you feel as a result of them. Do you feel tense? Do you feel happy? Do they distract you? When you are tense does this affect people around you? I would like you to become aware of this.

By watching your thoughts without reacting to them, you learn about the nature of thought and become less of a prisoner to it.

For example, when you are talking with somebody, do you have a lot of thoughts? When you are reading a book or doing a task, does thought after thought distract you? When you go for a walk in nature, is your attention in your head or are you really seeing, hearing and feeling what is going on around you? When you are driving, do you lose track of the journey and enter the stream of mind? When you are brushing your teeth, is that all you are doing or where is your attention? When you are eating a meal, are you enjoying each mouthful or did your mind take you over soon after the first bite? When you have breakfast, are you also reading the newspaper, the writing on the cereal box or whatever else is available? As you drink a cup of tea, are you really tasting what you are drinking, sip by sip? When you go to the toilet, are you really there or is your attention elsewhere?

Please do the above and, in every situation that you find yourself in, watch how you are thinking. Are you really living life or are you solely living in your head? Are you missing what is going on around you or are you really connected? Is your mind causing you torture and draining you of energy? Do you think to reach a conclusion or are your thoughts a merry-go-round with no finality? Be honest, as you are not alone.

Humans have lost the ability to control their minds. They have no idea of what is taking place in their mind. They are asleep.

Is the mind the absolute truth?

Many influences shape your life: events, TV, propaganda, literature, advertising, family, friends, parents, society, education and religion. All of these things develop and condition the programs of your mind. In turn, this influences how you act, react, perceive and interpret. Ultimately, no attitude, behaviour, thought or opinion is truly yours.

One child grows up with a parent who constantly fears poverty. Year in and year out, he listens to his father talk about a lack of money and all of his bills, and wonder aloud about what money is coming in the future and whether he will have work in a few months. His father is afraid to spend money for fear of the future. The child listens to this from day one to when he gains independence and leaves home. His father has a poverty consciousness and chances are that it will be passed onto the child. Later in life, whenever a decision is made relating to money, the child who grows into an adult will look through his poverty consciousness. Every time he receives a bill in the post, his stomach will tense. Anytime that he goes to the bank to deal with a small issue, he will worry about it beforehand. If someone overcharges him, he will get very agitated. He will make choices solely based on money. This person will constantly fear and worry about finances. A loss of money will be a great hardship to him.

Another child lives in a household of similar means but with a father who has a comfortable attitude about money. He is careful and does not overspend. He does his work and earns a living, even though sometimes it is not easy. Things always fall into place. This father does not constantly complain about a lack of finances. If he has a tight few months, he realises that this will change. This child will grow up to be an adult who does not fear for a lack of money.

The first child who grows into an adult will believe his viewpoint to be absolutely true. Tension, anger and arguments will arise if his partners' behaviours differ from his. The second child will grow into an adult without such heavy opinions regarding finance and money. Who is right? Who is wrong? Who is acting out of free will? Are you any different?

Our mind is shaped and conditioned by many factors over which we have no control. Many of our thoughts are shaped completely by our past, and are based on the opinions, habits, events and actions of other people. For most of us, we are living a life imposed by someone else. Do you think you are living a life free from the influences of others?

Don't accept what your mind throws up at you to be the absolute truth. We all form opinions about people, situations and events. But are these completely true or are they based on our past conditioning?

Most People are other people.
Their thoughts are someone else's opinions
Their lives a mimicry
Their passions a quotation

Oscar Wilde

How many times have you worried about something that turned out fine? How many times were you excited about something that turned out the opposite of what you hoped for? How many times did you form an opinion about someone, only to later realise that it was inaccurate? Are you living your own life or are you living the life of your parents? You think you have independence. Well, do you?

How could you be living a free life if you blindly follow your mind? Your mind is not you. It is a collection of the opinions of others. How on earth can this be truth?

CHAPTER 8
Individual madness

Are you always seeking the future?

When the boy is small, he is waiting to grow up to be a big boy. When he is a big boy, he is waiting to change schools. When he is in primary school, he is waiting to attend secondary school. When he is in secondary school, he is waiting to get a job or attend university. When he has a job, he is waiting to get married. When he is married, he is waiting to have children. When he has children, he is waiting for the children to get older. When his children are older, he is waiting to retire. When he is retired, he has little future left so he starts to dwell on the past. When he is young, he is anxious and thinks about the future. When he is old, he is depressed and thinks about the past. Life has passed him by, and by the time he realises this, it is too late. Don't wait for your life to change. Live it now.

Not only are we waiting for life changes, we are also seeking lifestyle choices.

"Oh, life will be so much better when I achieve this, that or the other. Oh, how wonderful life will be in six months. Oh, how happy I will be in my new car. I long for the future. My car is not the latest model. My house is not as nice or big as my friends. I was happy until I saw my friend's house, but now I am not happy. My house is not good enough."

"I made a mistake six months ago. I cannot live happily with my problem. The problem is so big. I am putting my life on hold until the problem is solved. I will be so unhappy until then. It is the future that I want. I will be only happy in the future."

When I get a new house, life is bliss for a few weeks. When I get a new car, I am so happy for a few weeks. When I get a new wife or husband, I don't know how I will ever have lived without this person – for a few weeks.

When my problem is sorted out, it will not be long before another surfaces.

Achievement of goals brings momentary happiness. As soon as we achieve, the mind sets another goal. Like the boy growing up, the goalposts keep moving. We can never catch up using this approach.

Set goals but keep your attention in the present. Don't be concerned about the outcome. Set the outcome aside as this will only take you into the future. In any event, having your full attention on the task at hand will generate a far superior quality of work.

Work on your goal but keep your attention immersed in the present moment and move with it step by step, frame by frame. Move simultaneously with time. You cannot live in the future, nor can you live in the past. The present moment is the only time you can live in.

We come into this world with nothing. We leave this world with nothing. In India, it is common practice for parents to advise their children to remain at a certain economic or social level for quite some time before moving on again. In other words, they are told not to get caught up with the feeding frenzy of consumerism that takes place in the West.

Advice like this, along with the practice of inner body awareness and meditation, has resulted in very low depression rates in India. Contrast this with the tension of man in the so-called developed world.

Is this his life?

Liam was one of the wealthiest property developers in Ireland throughout the economic boom. During mid-2009, an Irish bank sought to put him into bankruptcy.

The Pat Kenny morning radio show mentioned that a friend told Liam that it was "only money," to which Liam replied, "it's not only money, it's my life."

Is his perspective true? Yes, he spent years building his empire and it was tumbling down around him. That is difficult. But how is it his life?

For years, he might have invested a lot of time thinking about his life story. "Oh, what a wonderful man I am. How wealthy I am. I am worth so much money. I have big cars and property. Oh, people must think I am great. I am so clever." He reduced his life to a story.

Now, circumstances have changed and he can no longer live the story that he built up over the years. His lifestyle no longer coincides with his story. While this is not an easy life challenge, it is not his life. The story is nothing more than a figment of his imagination.

Of course, build up your business, make money, have a nice lifestyle. But don't get lost in it. Don't lose sight of the real you. Things come. Things go. Everything in life is a series of cycles.

Life is not about more money, more cars, more houses and more business. This is the human mind and not the real you. The human mind, especially the mind of the Western male, always wants more. More, more, more.

What is your story?

Our story is a fairytale of how we perceive ourselves. We think about our positive qualities and we think about our negative qualities. If thoughts about our positive qualities outweigh thoughts about our negative qualities, we are confident about ourselves.

If thoughts about our negative qualities outweigh our positive qualities, we lack confidence.

A negative story can be made up of constant thoughts about being fat or ugly or stupid, or not attractive to the opposite sex. Someone with an inferiority complex might have been told at one point how useless he is. He continues to run this thought over and over through his head. After a certain time, he acts according to this belief system that has been established. Over time, these thoughts become fixed and form his personality.

A positive story might be made up of how educated I am, how smart I am, how attractive I am, how large my muscles are, what a well paid person I am, how intelligent I am.

Both are stories and both are thoughts and figments of your mind. These stories are created through the repetition and reinforcement of thousands of the same thoughts. Your story is not real. Do you think it is the truth? What happens when your story changes?

What happens when the attractive person gets old and wrinkled? What happens when the wealthy person goes bankrupt? Why waste so much energy creating a story that is nothing more than a figment of the imagination?

My Negative life Story.

My tummy is too big.
My head is going bald.
I don't think I am good looking.
I cannot find a girlfriend.
Sure, how can I get a
girlfriend looking like this?
In work, people look at me.
They see my thinning
hair and big stomach.
I don't feel good about this
when I look at pictures in Hello
magazine, people look so good.
They look so much better than me.

My Positive life Story.

I have great muscles.
Everybody looks at me.
I am so intelligent.
I attended Trinity College.
How clever I am...
How good looking I am.
I am a wonderful person.
All the boys look at me.
All the girls look at me.
I'm just so sexy.
People envy me, oh what
a great feeling to get all
this attention. How nice
how happy I am, when
people give me attention.

131

When you create a story, you tend to act from that story instead of acting from free will. Therefore, your story restricts your freedom to act spontaneously.

Animals and nature do not create stories about themselves. A dog with three legs gets on with life. A fat horse is not too bothered either. An ugly crow has no problem waking up on a Monday morning. They live according to their true nature, which is absent of thought.

Living your life according to the story that you have created about yourself is not living. How can you experience life if your attention is constantly stuck in your head? Get out of your head and into life. Wake up from your living sleep.

Stop complaining

Watch how often you are unhappy with what is going on in your life. Become aware of how little things upset you. The more thoughts that you have running through your head, the more you get upset and frustrated by little things.

In every situation, you can always find something that is not how it should be. Children might be running around while you eat at a local café. Your partner might snore at night. The toilet seat might have been left up every time you use the bathroom. The coffee pot might be left on the counter every morning and might have left a stain. The weather is bad. The economy is in recession. You are stuck in traffic. Finances might be a little low. The shower leaks. The neighbour is an ass.

Are you constantly complaining about one thing or another? Complaining keeps you in a constant state of turmoil, as you don't want to accept the reality of this moment. You wish it to be different. Complaining is when you are not prepared to accept the current situation and you want something else. You are rejecting what is.

You have four options.

1. Accept the situation.

2. Remove yourself from the situation.

3. Change the situation.

4. If the time is not right to change the situation, drop the story and wait for the time to be right. Everything changes and this will change too. It is as it is.

CHAPTER 9
Society madness

Prozac me

A patient visits his doctor. He is complaining of constant noise in his head. He feels very down in the dumps, frequently cries and has constant chatter going on in his mind. He thinks that he is going mad. His constant thought and mind activity is making him crazy. The doctor listens for ten to fifteen minutes. Towards the end of the consultation, he takes out his prescription pad and writes a prescription for Prozac or some other legal drug to numb the person's mind.

The reality is that doctors don't know what causes depression. The medical model identifies depression as caused by a biochemical brain imbalance from a genetic defect. This is debateable.

In the words of Dr Terry Lynch in his superb book Beyond Prozac "Is the brain chemical imbalance the cause of the depression or the suicide, or is the imbalance produced by the long-standing emotional and psychological distress that person has endured often for many years?"

The amount of prescribed medication for depression, stress and anxiety has now reached epidemic proportions. Medication has one purpose and that is only to treat symptoms. Medication has a purpose only if the person is in danger of harming himself.

In simple terms, the mind is depressed with thought. Therefore, instead of numbing the mind with toxic medications, should we not attempt to give this person control over his thought processes? Allow the person to develop stillness of the mind. Stillness of the mind is achieved by watching and reducing the breath, feeling the inner body and keeping the attention in the present moment.

If drugs were not an option and stillness of the mind was taught in every school, we would have far less of a problem with mental health.

Millions of children and adults would be spared from suffering and be allowed to lead normal lives without being numbed by powerful medications that are very difficult to come off the longer one takes them. The Western health model is to create consumers. Profit, not health, is the first priority of drug companies.

Watching the body and mind is a challenge. Doing this takes time but gets to the root of the disquiet. Although meditation and medication differ by one letter only, they are miles apart.

Spiritualise me

Spirituality can be defined as the extent to which we stop thinking and connect with life. It is a widely expressed but much misunderstood word.

For centuries, people in Ireland strongly resorted to religion. Some of the motives were political, as religion was a way to differentiate ourselves from our colonisers. Other motives included fear of the Catholic priest with his threat of hell and damnation. A future in hell with raging fires was enough to drive us to Sunday mass.

For years, we left our substandard homes and took weekly refuge in the quietness of the church. We dressed up in our best Sunday suits. The church, with its stone surroundings, majestic belfry, high ceilings, solid wooden beams and marble floor was awe-inspiring. The mind stilled at such a sight.

Furthermore, belief in a higher being expressed through the form of a man-made institution reduced thought activity, just as a caring parent tells a child that everything will be okay and not to worry. "I believe in the Roman apostolic church."

Finally, the act of prayer, which involves repetitive words and sounds, further stilled the mind as attention was diverted to prayer instead of thought.

People left the church happy. They were lighter. Their thought activity was considerably reduced for an hour or so.

Newer generations in Ireland don't have the crutch of religion. With improved education and freedom to express one's opinion, most people have lost trust in traditional institutions. Nor is there a fundamental movement towards meditation.

Some youngsters get involved with sports, during which time their minds are at rest.

When one pushes the body in physical exercise, the mind stops.

However, others revert to alcohol or drugs. They replace the spirit from the church with the spirit from the top shelf. Both, by the way, still the mind. However, there is a large price to pay by stilling the mind with alcohol. Drink is a downer and causes depression the next day. Alcohol does nothing to address the racing mind and is just a temporary means of numbing the drinker.

The increased uptake of alcohol by many teenagers is not solely a result of peer pressure. They too have fear of the future regarding exams, getting a job, fitting into society and living up to the demands of looking attractive with perfect bodies. They are forced into the rat race whether they like it or not. This creates anxiety and, with no other outlet, alcohol and drugs are means of drowning out the mental commentary.

From speaking with alcoholics, the one thing they have in common is a racing mind. Alcohol is a means to escape anxiety. If no anxiety existed, the world would have far fewer alcoholics. Deal with anxiety by abandoning the spirit in the bottle and connect with true spirituality.

True spirituality is the degree to which you are out of thought and connected with life. The kingdom of heaven is within.

God is stillness of the mind, an inseparable oneness with life. God is within. God is not a plastic statue, picture frame, belief or thought. God is no thought. As the Bible states: "Be still and know that I am God."

Educate me

In Western civilisation, we attach importance to the ability to think. From an early age, we attend school to learn how to think, to decipher, to analyse, to examine and to investigate. We spend fifteen to twenty years in formal education developing this trait. Good students are rewarded and poor students are frowned upon. The idea of regurgitating information and critical analysis is the order of the day. An intelligent person is considered as one who has stored lots of information in her head. In comparison with our ancestors, we have a tremendous capacity to think. Being able to think is a wonderful aid to solving problems, making decisions and getting a job.

However, the downside to this is that we have lost control over our minds. This is the case with the vast majority of people, including those viewed as pillars of society, schoolteachers, university professors, priests and medical professionals. For the most part, they are living in their minds. The vast majority of them are asleep. Their lives are lived through their minds, making little direct connection with life.

Schools and universities develop the left side of the brain and abandon the right. Depression, anxiety and mental turmoil are all products of left-brain thinking. Meditation, feeling the inner body, following the breath and stilling the mind develop the right side of the brain. If you develop the left side of your brain through years of formal education, it is necessary to develop your right-hand side to restore the balance. Formal education teaches us how to think, but it does not teach us how to stop thinking. Thought after thought after thought is enough to make us go mad!

CHAPTER 10
Can you afford not to have a still mind?

Creativity

The discovery of a novel or relatively new idea or approach originates only from a still and quiet mind.

Thoughts are stale. All thoughts originate from past information and events. Nothing fresh arises from stale and useless thinking. When a person is asleep in thought, there is a very limited store of knowledge to glean from. When a person is outside of thought and directly in contact with life, he has universal intelligence at his disposal.

Some people are naturally more creative than others. Unknowingly, they have discovered the power of stepping outside of thought. Their insights and ideas are bright, unusual, fresh, different and shape the world we live in.

Schoolteachers and university professors have devoted their life to learning and teaching, yet they produce very few original or creative works. Universities are filled with thousands of students writing PhDs and masters theses, yet few people read them. They contain regurgitated information from the past.

The original works of Leonardo da Vinci, Michelangelo, Monet, Van Gogh, Cezanne, Yeats, Joyce, Beckett and others were not produced from stale and repetitive thinking of the mind. Universities and schools cannot take credit for their works. These masters could put their minds aside and allow their consciousness to become one with the universe. By tapping into this intelligence, their works were born. Develop your creative capacity by staying out of thought. Allow thought to drop and allow stillness to enter.

Watching the breath, feeling the inner body and connecting to life opens the floodgates for creative ideas. Original ideas are no longer an effort but result from a beautiful unfolding and tapping into the ether.

A still or noisy mind in the workplace

During my university years, I spent one summer in the beautiful town of Uppsala in Sweden working as a dishwasher. The kitchen was a busy place and served countless meals. One interesting observation was the state of minds of two chefs.

One chef would arrive and within minutes, he would be stressed. Meal tickets would be missed. Orders would be late and food would return cold. The chef would be working extremely hard but yet all of this happened. The kitchen was a mess.

Another chef would arrive to just as busy a shift. This chef remained calm, serving the same number of dishes. Seldom was food returned. The waitresses were happy as food was served on time and their tips were good. Both chefs received the same training and had about the same number of years of experience. What differentiated one chef from the other was his state of mind. The first chef's mind was overcrowded with thoughts, resulting in divided attention. A small percentage of his attention was actually on preparing the food while the remaining 90% was on a never- ending train of thought. What is the next dish? Do I have the ingredients? What the hell am I doing here? Another order in, how will I cope? How will I manage another order in?

A waitress returns with a cold sirloin steak. Pick it up, slap it on the floor a few times, scrape it off, place it in the microwave and send it back to the customer. To hell with that customer. Another order in, when is my shift over? I want to get out of this god-forsaken place. Another order in? Well, to hell with this.

The second chef was in the flow with a mind concentrated on preparing food. His mind was still and calm, which produced good concentration for the task at hand.

As he worked, he concentrated on whatever dishes he was making at that time. This allowed him to devote his full attention, resulting in less mistakes and higher quality. Incidentally, not only was the quality superior, it was also more efficient than the rushed and chaotic approach of the first chef.

Some people naturally have a still mind. Everybody has the capacity to develop a still mind. A still mind is reflective in anything you do. Only a still mind produces quality. You develop a still mind through meditation, feeling your inner body or following your breath.

Concentration

Concentration can be regarded as the ability to hold attention on an object or subject without internal distraction. Masters of any discipline have excellent concentration. The late George Best performed his game in the flow and without thought. Tiger Woods meditates and this is reflected on how focused he is during a game. Even if he has a bad shot, he has the capacity to control his mind and not allow this to affect the rest of his game.

Creative people have the capacity to concentrate and move, by choice, from periods of thought to no thought.

Poor concentration occurs when your mind is bombarded with one thought after another. For example, while reading, a thought will interrupt your capacity to follow the words every few seconds. By the end of the page, you will have forgotten much of what you have read. Worrying destroys your concentration, as your ability to focus is replaced by clouded thought. A child labelled with attention deficit disorder will constantly fidget and move about in parallel to the activity of her mind.

No matter what you do in life, concentration is paramount. If you are unable to hold your attention, your work will be substandard and of poor quality.

A person doing a task with an active mind is more concerned with getting to the end of the job and finishing it than on paying attention to the job itself. As this person does her work, 90% of her attention is on getting to the end of the task and only 10% is on focusing on the job. As she does her job, she will be rushed – in line with her mental commentary. She will miss parts, make mistakes, have poor attention to detail and

complete the work to a substandard level. In some instances, she will start the job and move on to another job before even completing the first.

Look at the quality of work from people with an active mind.

As you read this book, watch how many times your mind wanders. Good concentration is about being able to fix one's attention on something with unwavering thought for many minutes. Poor concentration is when one's mind can hold its attention for just a few seconds.

The more thoughts you have running through your head, the less concentration you have. The less concentration you have, the poorer your ability to hold your attention on something for a certain period. Improve your concentration by taking back control of your mind by reducing your breathing, following your breath or keeping your attention on your inner body.

NOTES:

CHAPTER 11
You know all of this!

Accept it as if you had chosen it so

When something in life does not go according to our expectations, we feel aggrieved. It might be a loss of money, children going astray, a partner deciding to leave you, losing your job or any other dilemma.

When confronted with this, we have two choices. We can either accept the dilemma or refuse to accept it.

By refusing to accept it, the mind creates mental turmoil. The situation has happened. It is as it is and, in many situations, there is little we can do to change it. What is within our complete control is our perception of the situation. Shakespeare's famous line, "nothing is good or bad, but thinking makes it so," rings so true. It is not the event itself that is the problem. It is our reaction to the event that determines our happiness. If we choose not to accept a situation, we generate conflict between what has happened and what we believe should have happened.

Depending on the level of intensity to which we refuse to accept, the mind may be energised for days, weeks or years to come. Life is often put on hold until the event sorts itself out. Ultimately, if we do not accept what has happened, we simply generate misery within ourselves.

Understanding the above is simple. It makes sense. But is the acceptance just through words or is the acceptance actual and outright?

"My partner has left me. Ok, I will accept that. I don't need the stupid idiot in my life anymore. I'm going to screw him for every penny he has and I hope the bitch that he ran off with also suffers. Yes, I will accept that he has left. He has left me stranded."

The above is a story. It is acceptance only in words. It is not peaceful acceptance. There is peace of the mind only when acceptance is outright, with no negativity for what has taken place. William James expresses it this way: "Be willing to have it so, because acceptance of what has happened is the first step in overcoming the consequences of any misfortune."

Feel your inner body. Reduce your breathing!

Shut the door to the past and move on!

Making mistakes is a significant human trait. The greatest people on earth have all had numerous setbacks and have made mistakes. If you make a mistake, analyse the past for just a short time. When you fail, it's okay to get upset or to feel down for a while.

Don't make the mistake something that you continuously live from. If you constantly think about a past mistake, you will develop it into something so big that it will wash over and affect every aspect of your life, and will only serve to increase your thought activity and create an agitated and distracted mind. A distracted mind will divide your attention every minute, every hour, every day.

At some point in the past, if you carried out an action that greatly hurt other people, understand that such action was based on the conditioning and beliefs of your mind at that time. Make amends if you can. Ask for forgiveness if possible. Your pain is there to give away.

Thirty years ago, it was customary in Ireland to have a few pints of alcohol and drive a car. Two local men from Dunboyne went to a football match in Trim. After the match, they had a few drinks. On the way home, they crashed their car and the passenger was killed. The driver, who was 35 years of age at the time, escaped with injuries. For the next thirty years until his death, the driver frequently thought about the accident. In his later years, he became depressed as a result of these thoughts. Yes, the man made a mistake and did an unintentional act. But the human mind turned this into thirty years of anguish. The driver was my father.

A child grows up in a housing estate where drugs are openly sold as the main form of income. From a young age, the child is immersed in this culture. The police are enemies and other people are a means to make money. When the child grows older, he peddles drugs.

The pusher sells a bad batch. A quiet 22-year-old buys drugs, develops permanent brain damage and is placed in life-long care. The 22-year-old is my brother.

Do you think the pusher sold the drugs with a free mind? Do you think a conscious choice was made? The pusher's actions were based on the conditioning of his mind at that time.

You might have done bad things in the past. You might have made terrible mistakes. But don't allow the past to totally consume your life. If you do, you will shut yourself off from life. Your mind is kept alive when it is allowed to dwell in the past or future. You can only think of either the past or the future. There is no room to think when your attention is absorbed in the present. See your mind as a moving right arm.

"What's done can't be undone."

— **WILLIAM SHAKESPEARE**

Stop stirring the problem

You have a bucket of muddy water and you would like the water to be clear. Therefore, you get a stick to stir the water in an effort to see the bottom. However, the more you stir the water, the more the sediment is agitated, further muddying the water.

This is the human mind. The water is muddy, which is akin to having a situation to be dealt with. Instead of stirring the water, we run the problem through our mind over and over in an effort to reach a solution. If we allowed the water to settle, the sediment would fall to the bottom of the bucket and the water would become clear. If we allow the mind to become quiet, it becomes clear and a solution can enter. There is no room for a solution to enter an agitated mind.

We tend to dwell on problems with thought after thought after thought. We go for a drive and think about the problem. We go for a walk and think about the problem. We lie wrapped up in our cosy beds at night and think about the problem. We talk with our friends and family and think about the problem.

Our decision-making process becomes clouded by the intensity of worry, fear and anxiety. The more we think about the problem, the larger it grows within our heads and the less likely the possibility becomes of finding an outcome.

Upon identifying the problem, connect with the problem instead of running away from it. See it as something that needs to be attended to. I'm not saying avoid the problem or ignore it and hope that it sorts itself out. What I am saying is make an attempt to solve the problem but without the mental commentary. See it head on for what it really is: something to be addressed.

Think about finding a solution for a few minutes, then drop the problem and enter stillness for a period until your mind settles.

Alternate between thinking and stillness. When the time is right, a creative solution will enter your mind. You will know it to be right. You will have a good feeling about it. A creative solution does not arise from constant thought. It arises from a gap in thought, from a cessation of thinking. Drop the belief that constant thinking will solve your problem, as it won't!

If you don't have a solution to your problem, put a request out there and feel that a solution is coming. Have faith that it will be sorted out at the right time. But whatever you do, don't keep running the problem through your head. Feel your inner body. Reduce your breathing!

> Do you have the patience to wait till the mud settles and the water is clear?
>
> Can you remain unmoving till the right action arises by itself?
>
> Lao-Tzu, Tao-te-Ching

The bullying child

Cian returned home from school. Some child was calling him names and he was upset and not at all happy. His mother instinctively tried to find out what happened, listened to him and then told him not to worry about it, that everything was okay and, if necessary, she would chat with his teacher. Cian went outside to play and soon forgot about the whole incidence.

What if this situation ended differently? What if Cian's mother was to repeatedly ask him, "What did he call you? When did he call you this? Why did he call you this? Where did he call you this? What did the other children do? Were they laughing at you? Did you like getting called names? How did you feel when he was calling you names?"

Imagine if she asked Cian the same questions half an hour later and again before dinner, again before he went to bed and first thing in the morning when he awoke?

Instinctively, Cian's mother would not do this. She knew that constant rehashing the situation would only turn the problem into a drama. If she asked Cian to repeatedly run the same situation through his head, he probably would have been unwilling to return to school the next morning.

Do you repeat the same stuff over and over in your own mind? Feel the inner body. Reduce your breathing!

Your enemies

Somebody did something to you once. This is bad enough, yet you choose to repeat the same problem over and over by running it through your mind, sometimes for weeks, months or years. It might have been a negative event, or person or situation. How long ago did it actually happen?

The event usually happens in a minute but you run it through your head over and over again. Drama is added through layers of thought. When somebody says negative things to you, learn from it if possible but then drop the mental baggage.

As you live in presence, you will become more conscious of the thoughts that take place in your mind. You will become aware of the effect of this on your body and will automatically drop the repetitive thoughts a lot earlier.

For past thoughts that you are repeating, wouldn't your enemy be delighted to know that you have kept your problems alive?

Feel the inner body. Reduce your breathing.

> A reporter once asked the Dalai Lama whether he held anger towards China. He replied "They have taken everything from us, should I let them take my mind as well?"

Positive thinking is limited at best

Thoughts create emotions and emotions create thoughts. One feeds off and contributes to the other. You are feeling down and emotionally drained. There is a dark cloud over you and the emotional charge has taken over. You feel like crying.

The more you think, the greater the emotion. In turn, this feeds your thinking processes. You don't like feeling this way and make an attempt to do something about it. You attempt to replace your negative thoughts with positive thoughts. This will not work.

You have too much of an emotional build up; therefore, no matter how hard you try to think positively, it will not happen and you will be even more unhappy. It wasn't enough that you felt unhappy in the first place, you now feel unhappy because you are unhappy.

If you are feeling down, don't make an effort to think positively. Instead, wait for the emotional build-up to dissolve. Accept that, at this time, you are moody, feeling down, unhappy and emotional.

Feeling this way is okay. Everybody has a day or two when things are just not right. If you have being feeling down for years, then make a conscious intention to bring as much attention to your inner body as often as you can throughout the day. Go for a walk, feel your inner body and reduce your breathing. Do Many Small Breath Holds throughout the day when you are sitting. Take attention out of your mind and aim to increase your Control Pause over time.

When you accept that this is how it is, pressure has lifted from you. Of course, it will take some time for the emotional charge to dissolve, but the more you stay in the now and follow your breath or feel your inner body, the quicker this will pass.

Happiness cannot be bought

Without a peaceful mind, your life is nothing. If it is agitated with thousands of thoughts and incessant worry, then it does not matter what cars, partner, money, house, job or title you have.

You fear for your financial future. You worry about it. Will I get by? Will I survive? You decide to do something, so you spend thirty years of your life in stress to reach financial security. Finally, you have arrived. Yet, your mind continues. You continue to worry. You worry about your health. You worry about the neighbours and what they think. You worry about your children. You worry about the unknown.

> You worry when you are unsecure.
> You worry when you are secure.
>
> Security does not bring
> about a peaceful mind.
> Only a peaceful mind brings
> about a peaceful mind.

Your mind is priority. Only with a peaceful and quiet mind will you enjoy life. If you work in a highly paid but stressful job, you might achieve certain material wealth, but is this at the expense of a quiet mind? You have achieved success but at what price?

Material wealth and titles are helpful, but all have limitations. Wealthy people are in and out of rehab, suffer from depression and fear of the future that at some point all of their achievements will disappear. An attractive person who depends on their looks will someday be unattractive. What happens to the wealthy person when the stock market crashes? Everything is subject to change. There is nothing that we can achieve in object form that will satisfy us permanently.

I'm not saying that you should not attempt to improve your lot. I am saying that you should know thyself by observing what is taking place in your mind and how it affects both you and others around you. Find yourself.

Material wealth is out of reach of most people living in the Eastern world. And yet, these people are lighter and happier that their Western counterparts. What is their secret?

The secret is the importance that the Eastern world places on the cultivation of a still mind. A quiet mind translates into lightness and happiness. A noisy mind translates into heaviness and unhappiness.

Achieve the nice car and house. Work in a top job. Yes, these are nice and make our lifestyle a little easier. However, they are secondary. What is primary is the extent to which you live outside of thought. You are entirely responsible for this and have a great deal of control over it.

Your true self is the only aspect that is constant. It does not change and remains the same regardless of what happens in the external environment. Tap into the real you by dropping the thought and living your life free from the filters of conditioning. Take off your sunglasses and see the light.

Feel the inner body. Reduce your breathing!

Are you generating peace or misery within yourself?

We need to have peace within ourselves before we can be at peace with others. How can you have peace with others when you are not at peace with yourself? Know thyself, not just at an intellectual level but at an experiential level. Observe yourself. Are you generating peace or misery within yourself?

When you generate negativity in your mind, you are bound to suffer. When your mind is peaceful and pure, you enjoy the kingdom of heaven within yourself.

Recognise how your mind affects the body and how emotions of the body affect the mind.

If you are angry with an enemy, you are the first victim.

If you are jealous of someone else, you are the first victim. If you hate someone else, you are the first victim.

If you seek revenge from someone else, you are the first victim.

These are the fundamental laws of life. If your mind is still, pure and free from tension, anger, animosity and jealousy, then life rewards you.

A prisoner convicted for many years can spend a lot of time thinking about getting revenge on the police officer who arrested him, the witness who testified against him, the judge who convicted him. But during that time, he is making his life a misery.

The more you think about revenge or hating your enemy, the more your body gets tense and the more your stomach

gets tied in a knot. You cannot have negative thoughts about someone else without these same thoughts having a negative effect on yourself.

You will be very surprised to see how situations sort themselves out when you are present with time. You will know what to do and can act without looking through thought. Problems do not sort themselves out by constant thinking and struggling.

I am not saying that you should do nothing and allow someone to walk all over you. If you need to challenge somebody, wait until the time is right. Don't challenge them when you are full of anger, because whatever you say in anger you will regret afterwards. Challenge them if necessary when you are still and present.

When the time is right, meet with the other person. Drop all prior thoughts of them and speak the facts. Explain the situation. By dropping all thought, you will remain calm and still. This is very powerful.

Finally, when you are present with time and connected with the greater intelligence of life, negative situations do not occur to the same extent. Life gets softer.

"I am the only
person in the world
I should like to know
thoroughly."

— OSCAR WILDE

Everything happens in the present. Nothing happens outside of the present. The present is the only thing that matters. When you pay good attention to your breath, to your inner body and to your five senses to the exclusion of thought, you are present. Whenever your attention is on your mind, you are out of presence.

Choose life or choose thought

We really need to choose life on a moment to moment basis. Keep asking yourself over and over again: are you wrapped up in thoughts or are you connecting with the reality of what is going on around you? It is that simple.

Relationships and thought are a good example. When we first meet our partners, life is a laugh, full of joy and fun. Over time we begin to better get to know our partners. We can often lose sight of their good points and start to dwell on their bad points.

We focus on the habits of the other person that annoy us: clothes are not put away, he/she spends too much money, is too tight with money, wastes electricity, is obsessed about saving electricity, likes to party too much, won't go out at all, watches TV too much, buys too much junk food, won't let himself go, has no interest in others, have little in common. We start to analyse and dwell on the differences and we run them over and over in our mind. We forget about our partner's good points as the bad points take over. Then, we meet our partners and see him or her through this collection of thought. We begin to argue and tension arises. Emotions run high and we get upset with each other.

This is a reflection of the mind. Little habits that before were endearing are now the cause of marital and relationship issues.

If your relationship has issues, then the next time you see that person, see him or her as if for the very first time. If you were not looking through the past, things would be different. People running on a train of thought think negatively about their relationships all the time. Then, when they see the person, they look through what they have been thinking about. How could you have a good relationship by looking through so much junk?

If you are not happy, you are spending too much time thinking. If you don't get on with members of the opposite sex, you are spending too much time thinking. If you hate your job, you are spending too much time thinking. If you feel unattractive, you are spending too much time thinking. If you think you are God's gift to women, you are spending too much time thinking. You are creating problems from your thoughts. If you just let your thoughts subside, you would have far fewer problems.

The answer is to not analyse the other person. Don't look through your collection of thoughts. Don't have a preconceived idea of him or her. See and really see. Hear and really listen. Feel and really feel. You will sense freedom when you get in touch with life, as life is the prime substance behind everything. The real world is life itself, not a collection of thoughts.

Some people never put down their thoughts, even for just a short while. These people completely miss out on life.

If you don't like your job, do it without thought. Don't let your mind in to analyse it and turn your workplace into a living hell. I spent a couple of years hating a job. I thought about it incessantly. All this does is get you down and keeps you trapped in the job. The more you think about how much you don't like your job, the less room you have for a solution to enter.

Very few thoughts will bother you if you are there step by step. Don't run on a collection of thoughts that you think it is. Following time step by step involves no thought. As time passes, go with time. Don't think of the future or worry about the past. The past is exactly where it is – in the past. There is little you can do to change it.

Thoughts are imagined as if they are real, but they are not real at all. Thoughts are stale. They are based on past conditioning and programs. But life is fluid and ever changing. You cannot get answers for something that is fluid by delving into old thoughts.

Feel your inner body. Reduce your breathing!

I cannot stop thinking

You might say that this all makes sense but it is impossible to stop thinking when things go wrong. Yes, I agree that doing it is more difficult. But at the same time, it is a lot easier than allowing the mind to run off on a worrying stream of thought. Of any 24 hour day, negative events generally account for a very small amount of time. It is our thinkaholic nature which prolongs the situation in our mind.

It is easier to build up your awareness by stilling the mind when things are GOING RIGHT FOR YOU. When life is running smoothly, make it a continued practice to observe your thoughts and bring COMPLETE attention to the present moment, or feel your inner body or follow your breath. The more you do this, the easier it is when things are not running so smoothly.

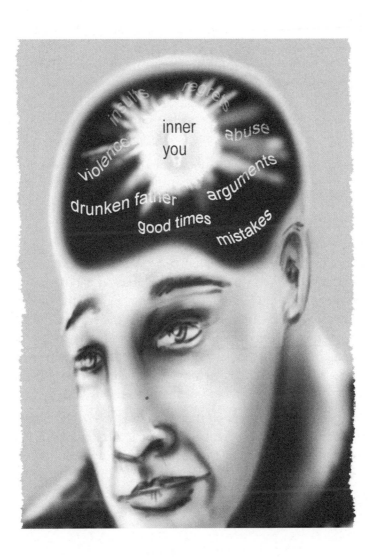

Old tensions dissolve

Past events and old thoughts that are buried well beneath the surface of the conscious mind will begin to appear as you calm your mind. By living in presence, watching your breath, feeling your inner body, the mind clears and past memories arise. Both good and not so good memories arise. From thirty years ago, you might remember a schoolteacher, childhood friends, an experience that happened while you were on holiday, or something somebody said to you.

Deeply rooted traumas might surface. As the old memories arise, just acknowledge them and let them pass, even stuff that has caused a lot of pain, such as emotional, physical or sexual abuse.

Just view these past traumas as thoughts. Observe them without attachment and let them pass. A mood change, emotional charge and short-term depression can be part of the process. If you feel down, accept it as part of the healing process. Feeling down is okay, as it is for the short term and will soon pass. Bringing acceptance to this helps speed the process. Deal with the past by living in the present. Doing this enables the old thought patterns that have shaped your life to dissolve.

The good news is that you don't have to analyse the past to address the past. You don't even need to understand it. Just live in the now and allow the past to surface and dilute.

We all need help from life

No matter how intelligent we are, we depend on life to help us along the way. We cannot do it alone, nor should we. All species with the exception of most humans allow life to assist them, care for them and provide for them. Birds, tigers, elephants, snakes, cats, dogs, seals, dolphins and whales are not worried about tomorrow, nor are they dwelling in the past. They have little fear except for brief moments when confronted by an animal of prey. Why are humans the exception? Why would life let humans down and look after every other living being?

You are not one with life if all of your attention is in your head. You are missing out on life and all that it is has to offer. Look at the state of the people around you. You will see how caught up they are in their heads thinking about the past or future and seldom having their attention in the now.

Life is not a collection of thoughts. Life has an immense intelligence that we seldom consider. Allow life to help you through life. Don't be constantly worried and afraid of whatever situation or event may unfold. Have trust in life and life will look after you.

Your job is to let life live through you. You enable this when you merge with your inner body or follow your breath. Your job is to live life, not to live in a collection of thoughts in your head. Living in your thoughts is living a life divorced from life.

LIFE

Let go of the wheel of life

In a sense, when we first let go of thought, we feel as if we are abandoning control. Society, education and other factors have conditioned us into believing that we always need to be thinking. The belief is that if we stop thinking, everything that we have ever accumulated or strived for will come tumbling down around us.

The belief is that our relationships will fall apart, our kids will go wild, our finances will dwindle.

Deep down, we believe that we must be thinking all the time. If this wasn't the case, why would we continue to do it? Here, I am asking you to take a chance on life and see how life looks after you. Forget about thought and join with life.

Let go of constant control and see what life brings you. It is the understanding that you literally have to do nothing and let life do it for you.

You are in this world to discover life. Have fun with it. Test it out. See if life is real. See if it is true. But you have to be willing to test it. Make the decision to change. You might have to start with very small areas.

If you are bored in your job, can you view it differently? Can you approach it without feeling that it is boring? Can you look at your wife or husband without seeing the negativity that you have running through your mind over the past few months?

Gently take back control of your mind. Watch your breath, feel your inner body, reduce your breathing. Do this for pockets of a few minutes many times throughout the day.

Especially do it while you are watching TV, driving your car, waiting in line at the post office, walking down the street, exercising, in bed at night. The more often you incorporate it into your life, the more you will continue with it.

It is you that stops yourself. See what life really provides you, as this will be far better than what is developed through a collection of thought. If you made a decision to choose life, then you would not choose thought.

How will you know if it is working? Quite simply, you will know by how you feel. You will feel alive and feel no tension. Your life will be softer and will unfold a lot easier.

If someone cuts you off while driving, you might honk your horn but you will return to stillness a lot quicker. If your mind is heavy, it is probable that you honk your horn and keep it pressed for a long time. If you are well immersed in stillness, you might have no need to honk. You let it go. You don't automatically react.

By feeling the inner body, you can sense how active the mind is. If the mind is stressed, your tummy will be tense and hard as a rock. You know the effect that anger has on your body and with this realisation, you don't reinforce it with continuous thinking. Instinctively, you are aware that to do so is harmful. After a while, the issue fades away. You understand the insanity of the human mind and do not identify with each thought as being real.

NOTES:

CHAPTER 13
The result

No more anger?

First, you watch your thoughts and emotions. You observe the interplay between your mind and emotions and how one influences the other.

You begin to realise the effect of your thinking. You bring your thoughts to the forefront of your mind as opposed to allowing them carry on unnoticed in the background. From this, you automatically exert more control over your thought processes. Just as you would immediately drop a hot item from your hand, the realisation that your mind determines your happiness is total and unquestionable. This is awareness.

You begin to understand your mind as a tool that you can use and, at the same time, that you gain more control over. While doing anything and between thinking for practical purposes, bring attention into your body and reduce your breathing. You follow each breath and feel the air shortage. You breathe through your nose at all times: during exercise, while sleeping and when engaged in any other activity. You feel your inner body throughout the day.

If you have a problem, you think for a while and then drop the thinking and merge with the inner body. You think for a few minutes and then stop thinking.

Does this mean that you never experience anger or emotions, or hostility or agitation? No.

You will have emotions and you will get angry, but less frequently. External circumstances and events will not affect you as before. The more stillness you bring into your life, the less you react and the quicker you overcome situations.

If someone cuts you off while driving, you might honk your horn but you will return to stillness a lot quicker. If your mind is heavy, it is probable that you honk your horn and keep it pressed for a long time. If you are well immersed in stillness, you might have no need to honk. You let it go. You don't automatically react.

By feeling the inner body, you can sense how active the mind is. If the mind is stressed, your tummy will be tense and hard as a rock. You know the effect that anger has on your body and with this realisation, you don't reinforce it with continuous thinking. Instinctively, you are aware that to do so is harmful. After a while, the issue fades away. You understand the insanity of the human mind and do not identify with each thought as being real. When one is aware of the effects of the mind and how it causes anger, hatred, tension and turmoil, you are able to automatically drop an issue a lot sooner.

Take responsibility for your own life

Depressed and anxious people also need to be accountable. After all, the problem and solution are both in the same place – your head. It is too easy to run to the doctor, throw money at him and allow him to push legal drugs on you without attempting to address the cause of the problem in the first place. Not all doctors are like this, but too many are. A person on continuous medication is great news for the Western health model. He or she is then a constant customer of pharmaceutical conglomerates and will use their products for the next few decades.

Some people tell me that they have tried breathing exercises and that they did not work. The simple answer to this is that they did not make a commitment to give it a good shot. They tried for a few brief moments or maybe a day or two, and then gave up. They lacked discipline. Well, I'm sorry to tell you that sometimes we need to put in effort to get somewhere. Watching your breath should not even be considered a task. Reconnecting with your body is a wonderful thing to do. It has taken many years of you adding thought after thought to get you to the point where you are today. It will also take a little time to reverse this habit. Like all habits, the mind wants to retain the status quo and, for a while, will be resistant to change. It is up to you and no one else to make this change.

For many people, Western society is a cop out. We have graduated into instant gratification, looking for the quick fix and not wanting to take responsibility for our own lives. If you don't give this a good shot, then I'm sorry to say that you have not suffered enough.

People often tell me that they do not have the time to watch their breathing or feel the inner body. Again, this is a cop out. Breathing or feeling the inner body can be applied during any activity or event.

I can honestly say that if you reduce your breathing and feel your inner body as often as possible for three weeks, you will be a changed person at the end of it. You will have a clarity of mind that you probably have not experienced since when you were a child. Remember, you once had clarity of mind. You once lived totally free from repetitive and incessant thinking. You once lived in a state of bliss. This has all been covered up by layers of conditioning and thought. Go back to your original state. Go back to how your life was during the first few years. See thought as something that you can choose to use for a practical situation. At other times, connect with the Now, your inner body and your breath, and the layers of thought activity and conditioning will dissolve as you no longer place attention on them.

It is not difficult to watch your breath and still your mind. This is the natural order of things, all we are doing is going home. What is difficult is living in the incessant noise of the head and accepting that whatever our mind throws up at us is true. I don't know how people live like this. I lived this way for many years and I suffered, was stressed and felt fear and anxiety. It is insane.

CHAPTER 14
What to do

The number of times you take attention out of your mind and put it onto your breath, your inner body or your senses— is far more important than the length of time occupied there. Be aware many times throughout the day.

A FOOLPROOF WAY TO QUIETEN THE MIND

If you find it difficult to still the mind by applying one of the practices, then apply two at the same time.

While reducing your breathing, place attention on your inner body.

While feeling your inner body, put your senses on what is taking place around you. See, listen and feel.

While you do what you love to do, apply it with your full senses to stay present with time.

It's about reducing your recurrent and repetitive thought activity.

Incorporating reduced breathing and stillness into your way of life will depend on how you are feeling. Using the Control Pause, state of health and age as a guide, the following approach will provide some insight.

Gentle approach: Not well, elderly or have a CP of less than 10 seconds

» Nasal breathe at all times including at night;

» Gently use the nose unblocking exercise if necessary;

» Watch your thoughts; know what is going through your mind and determine how your thoughts create your mood and how your mood creates your thoughts;

» Feel your inner body during many five-minute pockets throughout the day;

» As you sit in nature or pet an animal such as a dog or cat, feel your inner body;

» Relax your inner body. If your tummy is tense, encourage it to relax through mental chatter;

» Keep your breathing calm at all times; reduce your breathing by relaxing your tummy and chest;

» Avoid excessive talking or other activities that increase breathing;

» Eat food in small quantities;

» Never push yourself during physical exercise beyond the point where you lose control of your breathing;

» Practice the Many Small Breath Holds exercise throughout the day and ensure gentle reduced breathing with light to medium air shortage. For example, practice two thousand small breath holds and reduced breathing for blocks of five minutes many times throughout the day. (You don't have to count each breath hold; instead, do as many as possible.) The more severe your symptoms, the greater the number of breath holds and gentle reduced breathing you should undertake.

» Gentle walking each day with mouth closed.

Teenager approach

» Use the nose unblocking exercise if your nose gets blocked;

» Keep your mouth closed at all times, including during sleep;

» Observe the antics of your mind and be aware of repetitive thought activity; step outside of thought.

» Feel your inner body for pockets of five minutes many times throughout the day. In school, put 70% of your attention on listening to your teacher and the remaining 30% on your inner body or reduced breathing;

» Use Many Small Breath Holds when you feel stressed;

» When you have no symptoms, perform breath holds at different times throughout the day. For example, hold your breath while walking, on a trampoline, running, riding a horse or whatever physical exercise you like. While exercising, hold your breath for as long as possible without being stressed. At the end of the breath hold, calm your breathing as soon as possible.

» Be aware of the concept of reduced breathing and ensure that your breathing is quiet 24/7. It is not necessary to formally practice reduced breathing, but incorporate it into every activity you do. Remember that when you reduce your breathing, you are improving blood flow and oxygenation of the brain. You are also stepping out of thought during this time.

» Ensure that you relax your tummy and chest. Keep your chest still as you breathe!

An adult with a very busy lifestyle

» Reduce your breathing from the moment you wake up in the morning. For example, while lying in bed for a few minutes, reduce your breathing and create a need for air;

» Feel your inner body as often as you can throughout the day;

» Hold your breath and reduce your breathing. For example, while you are in the shower or washing your hair, hold your breath on the out breath and build up a good need for air;

» Reduce your breathing by relaxing your chest and tummy while you drive to work; ensure that your chest remains still;

» While you walk from your car to work, perform breath holds;

» Go for a 20-minute walk during your lunch break and do many breath holds throughout the walk;

» When you return from work, reduce your breathing in your car, while watching TV or reading a book, etc.;

» When faced with confrontation, bring attention immediately to your inner body. Start off first with small situations. In time, you will be calmer regardless of what is taking place around you.

» If you need to challenge somebody, wait until your anger has passed and approach the individual while keeping most of your attention on your inner body.

» Watch out for repetitive thought processes, especially the recurrent thoughts that take so much of your time, reach no conclusion, create anger and tension and drain you of energy.

Ideally, spend a cumulative 90 minutes per day divided among reducing your breathing, exercising with your mouth closed and feeling the inner body. The best time to reduce your breathing is first thing after waking, during the day and as the last thing at night. In addition, bring plenty of attention to your inner body. This will reward you many-fold.

Pay enough attention to your breathing to increase your CP by an extra 4 seconds each week. If your CP is not increasing from week to week, then pay more attention to your breathing or do the exercises formally by allocating sufficient time to them each day.

> **YOU HAVE TWO OPTIONS**
> Have a high CP and observe your mind
> OR
> Fight your symptoms for the rest of your life.
> Ignore it at your peril!

After a number of weeks practicing the exercises and with a CP of perhaps 20 seconds, you may reach a plateau where you seem to be making no improvement in your condition and your CP. This can happen regardless of the amount of time you spend at reduced breathing exercises. The best way to increase your CP from 20 to 40 seconds is to partake in physical exercise. If your Control Pause is stubborn, reduce your consumption of food as well to increase your CP more quickly.

In achieving a CP of 40 seconds, your mind will be considerably quieter. The attention you gave to your breathing while reducing it will also play a vital role.

Western society competes for our attention through advertising, social media and information overload. Give yourself some attention for a change. Your body is not just a head. It starts from your toes and continues right to the top of your head. Disperse your energy throughout and take back what is rightfully yours – your ability to be master over your mind!

My direct experience

When your mind is still and you give up trying, everything falls into place.

This is common reading in many self-help books. It was something that I came across time and time again. However, for many years I did not give it much heed as it flew in the face of everything that I had been taught over the years: that anything in life worthwhile is achieved through struggle, sweat and hard work.

When I look back at my life in the 1990s, it was an absolute mess. Today, I feel as if it is a past life. I was a chronic mouth breather, culminating with heavy breathing and regular sighing. I was a worrier and constant thinker. I would think and think and think. I was sure that what I was doing was beneficial and that it would propel me forward to get results, to achieve and to do well in life.

In 1992, I secured a place to attend Trinity College Dublin. Things were fine until I reached my third and fourth years. I was aware of the importance of such years and my ultimate goal was to get through each year without fail and to graduate. As a result, I spent every waking moment of the final two years thinking about getting through the exams, receiving my results, graduation day, my job after university and so forth. God only knows how many times I ran the same thoughts through my head – it must have been millions of times, and very possibly was. I reduced my third and fourth years to a constant struggle to finish and reach the end. I was stressed and anxious, and it was all self induced. Nobody else had put any pressure on me. I did it all to myself in the belief that it kept me on track to achieve. In many instances, I completely missed two years of my life as I reduced every moment to a means to achieve my goal.

I intensively studied for exams and spent lots of unproductive time in the library. I worked hard but not smartly. My retention levels decreased significantly given my already excessive thinking. It is difficult to make room for new information when the mind is already overactive. Few gaps existed in my stream of thought to allow new information to enter.

My first job was working in middle management in a USA car rental company. We were indoctrinated into the entire philosophy of the company. I was in my early twenties and an ideal candidate for being moulded and shaped to become a successful employee. After a few months of work, I began to hate the job. I hated the fact that systems and computers dictated and controlled everything that we did. I hated the constant pressure to achieve targets and to constantly better our results. I hated waking up on a Monday morning knowing that I had a full week's work ahead of me.

I ran this through my head all day. I found like-minded employees and we talked about what a crappy company we worked for.

From the age of 17 to 26 years, I made my life a living hell by constantly running thoughts through my head about the future, college, work, needing to buy a house. For some reason, I had an underlying belief that all of this thinking was beneficial. In fact, it was a form of torture that I subjected myself to on a continual basis.

Two factors changed my life. The first was discovering the work of Dr Buteyko. I switched from mouth to nasal breathing and learned to bring my breathing volume to more normal levels. I did have some ups and downs but this is a normal part of the process. Applying the Buteyko Breathing technique made an enormous difference in my anxiety level. In addition, my brain fog lifted, my asthma reversed, my snoring stopped and my energy levels improved dramatically. In fact my first night's sleep with my mouth taped was the best sleep I had had in about fifteen years.

The second was attending a workshop that included ideas about stilling the mind and living life. When I left, I walked down Grafton St, one of Dublin's main streets, with utmost clarity. Everything was so clear and alive. The sights and sounds had a sharpness and brightness that were completely new to me. It was as if my perception had improved many times. I felt at ease, relaxed and still. I knew that I had stumbled upon something but had no idea what it was.

The next morning I awoke and I was back to my usual self, with the continuous chatter of my mind. I had a day's work to do and targets to achieve. Whatever happened the previous night was just a glimpse, but it was enough to change my life.

A seed had been planted. I decided to go on a two-week course presented by a tutor immersed in stillness. After the two weeks, my mind was emptied of the self-torture that I had endured for so many years. Nothing new was added. Instead, I allowed layers of conditioning and thoughts that I had to dissolve.

I had far more peace than I had ever experienced before. As the days passed, the feeling of stillness and inner body energy intensified.

When I returned home after the two weeks, a massive weight had been lifted from me. For the first time, I realised that the nightmare I was living was as a result of my own thoughts. After a number of months, the intensity decreased but the stillness remained. I continued along my path of watching my mind, following my breath and keeping my mind still. I made a point of taking a short drive from my house to the Phoenix Park in Dublin, where I could sit in stillness with nature for an hour or so every couple of days.

After experiencing life-changing health benefits from Buteyko Breathing, I decided to train in the method. By March 2002, I was a certified practitioner and accredited by the founder of the method, Professor Buteyko. I commenced Buteyko courses in Ireland and within two years received considerable media coverage and attention. Now, thirteen years later, my work takes me around the world. I have written seven books, which have become very popular sellers, and have reached out to tens of thousands of people.

In 2005, I married my sweetheart, Sinead, and we bought a stone cottage in a most secluded and beautiful part of Connemara, Co Galway. The house is in the midst of stillness. I have no immediate neighbours and experience absolute quietness.

I have not achieved very much in the area of wealth or finance, but at the same time have no worries over money. What I have achieved is an excellent quality of life. I live in a beautiful setting with a beautiful person, and I love my work. Even if I win the lotto tomorrow, I would continue doing what I do. I left the rat race and am in charge of my own destiny. I am stress-free and honestly believe that no amount of money is worth a stressful life.

Of course, in life things are subject to change. I experienced a little stress while dealing with local rogue builders when we renovated the cottage. I lost my father rather unexpectedly in 2005 and nearly lost my brother a few years earlier. However, all of these things were a lot softer and easier to cope with. In fact, I could not imagine getting through any of them if I had been living my old way.

My point in writing the above is to explain to you that, in the last decade, my life has flowed so much easier and with far more joy than ever before. Furthermore, the only thing I did differently was to correct my breathing, reduce my thought activity and connect with life itself. Instead of struggling, and striving to achieve and succeed, life has come to help me. This might sound cosmic or strange to many readers, and I have no idea what is happening. It does not make logical sense and so much of our world is based on logic. However, I'm not too concerned about that. All I know is that when my thought activity reduced, my life unfolded beautifully around me. Helpful things happened. The right people came along. Ideas came to mind. When I allowed life to happen and did not constantly try to control it with excessive thoughts, ideas came and I seemed to know what to do. You can too!

Most people go through life asleep.

Every moment, their attention
is spent in their head.

When attention is in their head,
it is not possible to fully relate to life.

They are on autopilot, running their lives
according to the nonsense originating in
their minds, according to the thoughts and
opinions of others.

As long as your attention is on observing
your breath, or on feeling your inner body,
or is completely on your senses,
you are set free.

It is that simple.
No longer are you reinforcing the insanity.
Step out of thought and live life.

NOTES:

Recommended reading and viewing

The Oxygen Advantage: The Simple, Scientifically Proven Breathing Techniques for a Healthier, Slimmer, Faster, and Fitter You by Patrick McKeown

Buteyko Mindfulness Method Online Course; Calm your mind, improve concentration, live in the moment, and enjoy freedom from ADD, stress, panic attacks and depression by Patrick McKeown

Buteyko Clinic DVD set of DVD, CD & Manual – Complete instruction as presented by Patrick McKeown

Buteyko Kids DVD set of DVD & Manual – Complete instruction as presented by Patrick McKeown

Asthma Free naturally by Patrick McKeown

ABC to be Asthma free – How to teach young children by Patrick McKeown

Buteyko App with videos, voice recording, counter timer and alarm reminder for Android or iPhone. Available from ButeykoClinic.com, Amazon.com or Apple store.

All books are available from www.buteykoclinic.com, www.amazon.co.uk or www.amazon.com

Websites to visit

www.OxygenAdvantage.com
Dedicated to improving sports performance.

www.ButeykoClinic.com
Worldwide list of practitioners including Europe, North America, and Asia, practitioner training, videos of Dr Buteyko.

www.ButeykoDVD.com
Authors' Buteyko DVD, books, online courses and free video segments.

www.Buteyko.co.uk
Buteyko practitioners in UK.

www.TomHerronExperience.com
Buteyko Northern Ireland

www.CorrectBreathing.com
Carol Baglia, USA Buteyko practitioner

www.AsthmaCare.us
Eugenia Malyshev, USA Buteyko practitioner

References

Chapter two—The Buteyko Method

1. The American Journal of Medicine; December 1986; Volume 81; p989. Hyperventilation Syndrome and Asthma. (Demeter, Cordasco.)

2. Cited in Multidisiplinary approaches to breathing disorders by Leon Chaitow, Dinah Bradley and Christopher Gilbert.

3. Gibbs DM 1992 Hyperventilation induced cerebral ischemia in panic disorder and effects of nimodipine. American journal of Psychiatry 149: 1589-1591

4. Ball, Shekhar A 1997 Basilar artery response to hyperventilation in panic disorder. American journal of psychiatry 154 (11): 1603-1604

5. Balestrino M, Somjen GG, Concentration of carbon dioxide, interstitial pH and synaptic transmission in hippocampal formation of the rat, J Physiol 1988, 396: 247-266.

6. Huttunen J, Tolvanen H, Heinonen E, Voipio J, Wikstrom H, Ilmoniemi RJ, Hari R, Kaila K, Effects of voluntary hyperventilation on cortical sensory responses. Electroencephalographic and magnetoencephalographic studies, Exp Brain Res 1999, 125[3]: 248-254.

7. Artour Rakhimov Ph.D, Normal Breathing- The key to vital health

8. The Hyperventilation Syndrome, Robert Fried

9. Hyperventilation: the tip and the iceberg by L.C. Lum Journal of Psychosomatic Research, Vol. 19, pp. 375 to 383. Pergamon Press, 1975. Printed in Great Britain

Acknowledgements

A number of people were instrumental in the creation of this little book.

To Karen Kolb, Joseph Lawlor, Valerie Kerr, Eileen O' Connor and Kevin Kelly for their feedback and input. A special thanks to Louise George for her detailed analysis and suggestions. I am deeply indebted to Aurora Pérez Machio for her work in creating a wonderful cover and to Tracy for her work in editing and proofing the text.

Thank you, Rebecca Burgess for drawing the illustrations.

I would also like to thank everybody who has attended my courses over the past eight years. To fellow practitioners Tom Herron, Linda Meads, Peter Kolb, Alex Spence, Artour Rakhimov, Chris Bauman and more – thank you for your contribution to Buteyko in the Western world.

Finally, thank you Sinead for your smile.

Diary of Progress (Adults—Page 1)

Date																
Time																
Pulse																
CP																
RB 4 min																
CP																
RB 4 min																
CP																
RB 4 min																
CP																
RB 4 min																
CP																
RB 4 min																
Pulse																

Rest for one minute before taking CP. Alternatively, download the ButeykoClinic Self Help Program APP from ButeykoClinic.com or iTunes

Diary of Progress

(Adults—Page 2)

Date														
Time														
Pulse														
CP														
RB 4 min														
CP														
RB 4 min														
CP														
RB 4 min														
CP														
RB 4 min														
CP														
RB 4 min														
Pulse														

Rest for one minute before taking CP. Alternatively, download the ButeykoClinic Self Help Program APP from ButeykoClinic.com or iTunes

Diary of Progress

Date																
Time																
Pulse																
CP																
RB 4 min																
CP																
RB 4 min																
CP																
RB 4 min																
CP																
RB 4 min																
CP																
RB 4 min																
Pulse																

Rest for one minute before taking CP. Alternatively, download the ButeykoClinic Self Help Program APP from ButeykoClinic.com or iTunes

Diary of Progress (Adults—Page 4)

Date															
Time															
Pulse															
CP															
RB 4 min															
CP															
RB 4 min															
CP															
RB 4 min															
CP															
RB 4 min															
CP															
RB 4 min															
Pulse															

Rest for one minute before taking CP. Alternatively, download the ButeykoClinic Self Help Program APP from ButeykoClinic.com or iTunes